# RETHINKING PROOF

## with

**THE GEOMETER'S SKETCHPAD**®

*MICHAEL D. DE VILLIERS*

**Key Curriculum Press**
Innovators in Mathematics Education

| | |
|---|---|
| **Project Editors** | Daniel Ditty, Masha Albrecht |
| **Editorial Consultants** | Dan Bennett, Daniel Scher |
| **Editorial Assistant** | Erin Gray |
| **Production Editor** | Kristin Ferraioli |
| **Copy Editor** | Erin Milnes |
| **Production Director** | Diana Jean Parks |
| **Text Design** | Ann Rothenbuhler |
| **Technical Illustration** | Kirk Mills |
| **Photo Credits** | James Browne |
| **Cover Design** | Kavitha Becker |
| **Cover Photo** | Fred Otnes |
| **Prepress and Printer** | Data Reproductions |
| | |
| **Executive Editor** | Casey FitzSimons |
| **Publisher** | Steven Rasmussen |

®The Geometer's Sketchpad, ®Dynamic Geometry, and ®Key Curriculum Press are registered trademarks of Key Curriculum Press. ™Sketchpad is a trademark of Key Curriculum Press. All other trademarks in this book are the property of their respective holders.

**Limited Reproduction Permission**
© 2003 by Key Curriculum Press. All rights reserved. The publisher grants the teacher who purchases *Rethinking Proof with The Geometer's Sketchpad* the right to reproduce material for use in his or her own classroom. Unauthorized copying of *Rethinking Proof with The Geometer's Sketchpad* constitutes copyright infringement and is a violation of federal law.

**Rethinking Proof with The Geometer's Sketchpad CD-ROM**
Key Curriculum Press guarantees that the *Rethinking Proof with The Geometer's Sketchpad* CD-ROM that accompanies this book is free of defects in materials and workmanship. A defective disk will be replaced for free if retuned within 90 days of the purchase date. After 90 days, there is a $10.00 replacement fee.

Key Curriculum Press
1150 65th Street
Emeryville, CA 94608
510-595-7000
editorial@keypress.com
http://www.keypress.com

Printed in the United States of America    10 9 8 7 6 5 4 3 2    09 08 07 06    ISBN 1-55953-646-2

# ACKNOWLEDGMENTS

The activities and underlying philosophy of this book have been continuously shaped by my involvement with the teaching and learning of proof in geometry for over 20 years. This involvement has been as a secondary-school teacher, a researcher, and a lecturer to pre-service and in-service teachers at the university level. The University of Stellenbosch Experiment in Mathematics Education (USEME) provided me with an invaluable theoretical and experimental foundation (see Human and Nel 1989, 1997).

I am particularly indebted to the many students over the years whom I have been privileged to teach and to learn from. There are too many memorable learning incidents to mention here, but I would like to mention just two. In 1997, a group of my post-graduate students using Sketchpad™ were led to discover that the lines *FB, DC,* and *EA* were always concurrent for any triangle *ABC* with equilateral triangles on the sides as shown in Figure 1. They were then sent home with the challenge of finding an explanation (proof) for why this was true (no hints or guided worksheets were provided). Although they did not succeed in proving the concurrency on their own, two students, Mthembeni Mhkize and Zwelibanthu Zuma, in their proof attempt noticed the congruency of triangles *DCB* and *AEB*, as well as triangles *FBA* and *CDA*, arriving at the logical conclusion that line segments *FB, DC,* and *EA* must be equal. To me this is

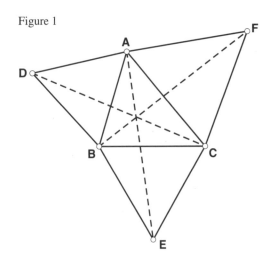

Figure 1

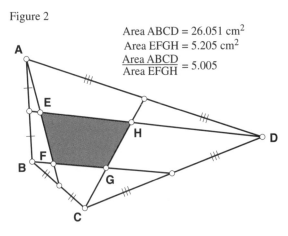

Figure 2

Area ABCD = 26.051 cm²
Area EFGH = 5.205 cm²
$\dfrac{\text{Area ABCD}}{\text{Area EFGH}} = 5.005$

an excellent example illustrating the *discovery* function of logical reasoning (proof). Although the discovery is not original (for example, see Coxeter and Greitzer 1967, 82–83), it was certainly experienced as such by the two students.

In 1998, one of my undergraduate students, Sylvie Penchaliah, made the following (unintended) conjecture in relation to the Sketchpad sketch shown in Figure 2 (compare with the Areas activity): for any convex quadrilateral *ABCD*, the area of $ABCD \geq 5 \cdot EFGH$. So far, neither my students, nor I, nor some colleagues to whom I've mentioned the conjecture, have been able to prove it, although we're pretty convinced it is true. (Unfortunately, the algebra gets very messy, and at this stage it seems unlikely we could produce a short, elegant proof— algebraic or geometric. See Teacher Notes to the Areas activity for an update on this conjecture.)

It is experiences like these more than anything, that motivated me to write this book. Support from a learning psychology perspective to the approach advocated in this book have been provided by M.Ed. research reported in Mudaly and de Villiers (2000), as well as in Govender and de Villiers (2002). While the first study explored students' needs for conviction and explanation within a dynamic geometry context, the second study found the systematization activities in Chapter 5 very useful in changing prospective mathematics teachers' understanding of definitions and helping them to develop their own proficiency in defining quadrilaterals.

I am also thankful to the many colleagues, both here in South Africa and abroad, from whom I have learned a great deal. In particular, thanks to Mark Evans at Kloof High School, KwaZulu-Natal, and Bruce Cohen at Lick Wilmerding High School in San Francisco, California, and their geometry students for welcoming me into their classrooms and giving me feedback on activities. Thanks also to my family who have patiently endured the many hours spent on the development, testing, and refinement of the activities. Lastly, I wish to thank Masha Albrecht and Dan Bennett who both did such an excellent job in editing and polishing my rough ideas, manuscripts, and sketches. Also warm thanks to Dan Scher and Dan Ditty for assisting with this revision for Sketchpad 4. Without their assistance, encouragement, and expertise, this book would not have been realized.

Michael D. de Villiers

The development and testing of these activities were partially funded by a grant from the National Research Foundation (NRF), Pretoria, and forms part of the Spatial Orientation and Spatial Insight (SOSI) Project, coordinated by Prof. Dirk Wessels (University of South Africa), Dr. Hercules Nieuwoudt (Potchefstoom University of Christian Higher Education), and Prof. Michael D. de Villiers (University of Durban-Westville). The opinions expressed are those of the author and project team, and not necessarily those of the NRF.

## ABOUT THE AUTHOR

Michael D. de Villiers is associate professor of mathematics education at the University of Durban-Westville, South Africa. His major research areas are geometry, the nature and philosophy of mathematics, and applications of school mathematics. From 1988 to 1997 he was editor of *Pythagoras,* the journal of the Association for Mathematics Education of South Africa (AMESA).

Since 1998, he has been editor of the *KZN AMESA Mathematics Journal,* and vice chair of the South Africa Mathematics Olympiad. Several articles on mathematics and mathematics education along with corresponding Sketchpad sketches are available for download on his Web site, http://mzone.mweb.co.za/residents/profmd/homepage.html. His e-mail address is profmd@mweb.co.za.

# CONTENTS

© 2003 Key Curriculum Press

In a recent article submitted to *Philosophae Mathematicae* (in press), Rehuda Rav poses the interesting situation of our having access to an all-powerful computer called PYTHIAGORA with which we can quickly check whether any conceivable mathematical conjecture is true or not. Would such a powerful tool spell the end of proof as we know it today?

Perhaps surprisingly to non-mathematicians, the answer to this question is a resounding *"No."* As Rav points out, it is quite often irrelevant in mathematics whether a particular conjecture is true or not. He gives the example of the still unproved Goldbach conjecture, which has been the fundamental catalyst for the development of major new theories as mathematicians search for a proof:

> *Look at the treasure which attempted proofs of the Goldbach conjecture has produced, and how much less significant by comparison its ultimate 'truth value' might be! . . . Now let us suppose that one day somebody comes up with a counter-example to the Goldbach conjecture or with a proof that there exist positive even integers not representable as a sum of two primes. Would that falsify or just tarnish all the magnificent theories, concepts and techniques which were developed in order to prove the now supposed incorrect conjecture? None of that. A disproof of the Goldbach conjecture would just catalyze a host of **new** developments, without the slightest effect on hitherto developed **methods** in an attempt to prove the conjecture. For we would immediately ask new questions, such as to the number of 'non-goldbachian' even integers: finitely many? infinitely many? . . . New treasures would be accumulated alongside, rather than instead of the old ones—thus and so is the path of proofs in mathematics!* (emphasis added)

A little further on Rav emphasizes that proofs rather than theorems are the bearers of mathematical knowledge:

> *Theorems are in a sense just tags, labels for proofs, summaries of information, headlines of news, editorial devices. The whole arsenal of mathematical methodologies, concepts, strategies and techniques for solving problems, the establishment of interconnections between theories, the systematization of results—the entire mathematical know-how is embedded in proofs. . . . Think of proofs as a network of roads in a public transportation system, and regard statements of theorems as bus stops; the site of the stops is just a matter of convenience.*

In a similar vein, the research mathematician Gian-Carlo Rota (1997, 190) pointed out, regarding the recent proof of Fermat's Last Theorem, that the value of the proof goes far beyond that of mere verification of the result:

> *The actual value of what Wiles and his collaborators did is far greater than the mere proof of a whimsical conjecture. The point of the proof of Fermat's last theorem is to open up new possibilities for mathematics. . . . The value of Wiles's proof lies not in what it proves, but in what it opens up, in what it makes possible.*

Two important ideas that clearly emanate from the above quotes are, first, that proofs are an indispensable part of mathematical knowledge and, second, that their value goes far beyond the mere verification of results. The first idea has obviously been a major motivating factor for writing this book, particularly in view of the possible misconception that powerful new computer tools like The Geometer's Sketchpad™ are making proof obsolete. Although such tools enable us to gain conviction through visualization or empirical measurement, proofs are still as important as ever. As alluded to in the second idea, proofs are extremely valuable since they can provide insights, lead to new discoveries, or assist systematization. These multiple roles of proof are the main ideas around which this book is organized. In many respects, this book provides a radical departure from traditional approaches to proof, which have almost exclusively focused only on the verification function of proof. Instead, here proof is introduced in Chapter 1 as a means for explaining results that have already been experimentally verified on Sketchpad™. Subsequent chapters highlight the discovery, verification, challenge, and systematization functions of proof. These functions of proof are discussed more fully in the section The Role and Function of Proof with Sketchpad on pages 5–10. That section is recommended background reading to the activities.

Other recommended background reading is the section The van Hiele Theory—Defining and Proving Within a Sketchpad Context, on pages 11–20, which places the learning and teaching of proof within the wider context of the meaningful learning of geometry. That section also focuses in some detail on the mathematical process of defining, arguing that students should not be provided with ready-made definitions, but need to be actively engaged in definition construction.

## SUGGESTED SEQUENCES

Because the activities have been grouped around different functions of proof, I don't suggest that you necessarily work through them in the order in which they appear in the book. The following tables show three different suggestions for sequencing activities: one complete (C), one medium (M), and one short (S). The numbers in each column indicate a suggested order. You should, however, feel free to sample activities and sequence them in your own order of preference, provided that students complete prerequisite activities or have prerequisite knowledge.

| Proof as Explanation | Complete | Medium | Short |
|---|---|---|---|
| Distances in an Equilateral Triangle | 1 | 1 | 1 |
| Water Supply I: Four Towns | 2 | 2 | 2 |
| Water Supply II: Three Towns | 3 | 3 | 3 |
| Triangle Angle Sum | 4 | 4 | 4 |
| Quadrilateral Angle Sum | 5 | 5 | 5 |
| Crossed Quadrilateral Sum | 6 | | |
| Isosceles Trapezoid | 7 | 6 | |
| Cyclic Quadrilateral | 14 | | |
| The Center of Gravity of a Triangle | 17 | 13 | |

| Proof as Discovery | C | M | S |
|---|---|---|---|
| Kite Midpoints | 8 | 7 | 6 |
| Logical Discovery | 11 | 10 | 9 |
| Isosceles Trapezoid Midpoints | 12 | 11 | |
| Logical Discovery: Circum Quad | 16 | | |

| Proof as Verification | C | M | S |
|---|---|---|---|
| Areas | 9 | 8 | 7 |
| Varignon Area | 10 | 9 | 8 |
| Logical Paradox | 13 | 12 | |
| Cyclic Quadrilateral Converse | 15 | | |
| Concurrency | 18 | 14 | |
| Triangle Altitudes | 19 | 15 | |
| Light Ray in a Triangle | 20 | | |
| Parallel Lines | 23 | | |

| Proof as Challenge | C | M | S |
|---|---|---|---|
| Parallelogram Angle Bisectors | 21 | 16 | |
| Parallelogram Squares | 22 | 17 | |
| The Fermat-Torricelli Point | 24 | | |
| Airport Problem | 25 | | |
| Napoleon | 26 | | |
| Miquel | 27 | | |

| Proof as Systemization | C | M | S |
|---|---|---|---|
| Reasoning Backward: Triangle Midpoints | 28 | 18 | 10 |
| Reasoning Backward: Parallel Lines | 29 | | |
| Systematizing Rhombus Properties | 30 | 19 | |
| Systematizing Isosceles Trapezoid Properties | 31 | | |

© 2003 Key Curriculum Press

# The Role

of Proof

That students have difficulty perceiving a real need for proof is well known to all high school teachers and is identified without exception in all educational research as a major problem in the teaching of proof. Who has not yet experienced frustration when confronted by students asking "Why do we have to prove this?" The following conclusion by Gonobolin (1954, 61) exemplifies the problem:

> . . . the pupils . . . do not . . . recognize the necessity of the logical proof of geometric theorems, especially when these proofs are of a visually obvious character or can easily be established empirically.

According to Afanasjewa in Freudenthal (1958, 29) students' problems with proof should not simply be attributed to their slow cognitive development (for example, an inability to reason logically), but also to the fact that they may not see the *function* (meaning, purpose, and usefulness) of proof. In fact, several recent studies in opposition to Piaget have shown that very young children are quite capable of logical reasoning in situations that are real and meaningful to them (Wason and Johnson-Laird 1972; Wallington 1974; Hewson 1977; Donaldson 1979). Furthermore, attempts by researchers to teach logic to students have frequently provided no statistically significant differences in students' performance and appreciation of proof (Deer 1969; Walter 1972; Mueller 1975). More than anything else, it seems the fundamental issue at hand is that the appropriate motivation for learning the various functions of proof is not perceived by students.

The question is, however, "What functions does proof have within mathematics itself that can potentially be utilized in the mathematics classroom to make proof a more meaningful activity?" The purpose of this section is to describe some important functions of proof, and briefly discuss some implications for the teaching of proof.

## THE FUNCTIONS OF PROOF IN MATHEMATICS

Traditionally the function of proof has been seen almost exclusively as being to *verify* the correctness of mathematical statements. The idea is that proof is used mainly to remove either personal doubt or the doubt of skeptics, an idea that has one-sidedly dominated teaching practice and most discussions and research on the teaching of proof. For instance, according to Kline and Alibert:

> A proof is only meaningful when it answers the student's **doubts,** when it proves what is not obvious. (Kline 1973, 151; emphasis added)

> The necessity, the functionality, of proof can only surface in situations in which the students meet **uncertainty** about the truth of mathematical propositions. (Alibert 1988, 31; emphasis added)

Hanna and Volmink also appear to define proof only in terms of its verification function:

> A proof is an argument needed to **validate** a statement, an argument that may assume several different forms as long as it is convincing. (Hanna 1989, 20; emphasis added)

> Why do we bother to prove theorems? I make the claim here that the answer is: so that we may **convince** people (including ourselves) . . . we may regard a **proof as an argument sufficient to convince a reasonable skeptic.** (Volmink 1990, 8, 10; emphasis added)

Although many authors (for example, van Dormolen 1977, van Hiele 1973, and Freudenthal 1973, and others) have argued that one's need for deductive rigor may undergo change and become more sophisticated with time, their viewpoint remains that the function of proof is mainly that of verification. For example:

> . . . to progress in rigor, the first step is to **doubt** the rigor one believes in at this moment. Without this **doubt** there is no letting other people prescribe oneself new criteria of rigor. (Freudenthal 1973, 151; emphasis added)

Many authors have also proposed specific stages in the development of rigor, for example, Tall (1989, 30) proposes three stages in putting forth a convincing argument, namely the convincing of oneself, the convincing of a friend, and the convincing of an enemy. Although these are extremely useful distinctions, the proposal considers only the verification function of proof.

Note: This section is a revised version of an earlier article by the author titled "The role and function of proof in mathematics," *Pythagoras* 24 (Nov 1990): 17–24. It is reproduced here with permission of the Association for Mathematics Education of South Africa.

However, as pointed out by Bell (1976, 24) this view of verification/conviction as the the main function of proof "avoids consideration of the real nature of proof," since conviction in mathematics is often obtained "by quite other means than that of following a logical proof." Therefore the actual practice of modern mathematical research calls for a more complete analysis of the various functions and roles of proof. Although I lay claim to neither completeness nor uniqueness, I have found the following model for the functions of proof useful in my research over the past few years. It is a slight expansion of Bell's (1976) original distinction between the functions of verification, illumination, and systematization. The model is presented here (in no specific order of importance) and discussed further on:

- *verification* (concerned with the truth of a statement)
- *explanation* (providing insight into why it is true)
- *discovery* (the discovery or invention of new results)
- *systematization* (the organization of various results into a deductive system of axioms, major concepts, and theorems)
- *communication* (the transmission of mathematical knowledge)
- *intellectual challenge* (the self-realization/fulfillment derived from constructing a proof)

## PROOF AS A MEANS OF VERIFICATION/CONVICTION

With very few exceptions, mathematics teachers seem to believe that only proof provides certainty for the mathematician and that it is therefore the only authority for establishing the validity of a conjecture. However, proof is not necessarily a prerequisite for conviction—to the contrary, conviction is probably far more frequently a prerequisite for the finding of a proof. (For what other weird and obscure reasons would we then sometimes spend months or years trying to prove certain conjectures, if we weren't already convinced of their truth?)

The well-known George Polya (1954, 83–84) writes:

> . . . having verified the theorem in several
> particular cases, we gathered strong inductive
> evidence for it. The inductive phase overcame our
> initial suspicion and gave us a strong **confidence** in
> the theorem. Without such **confidence** we would
> have scarcely found the courage to undertake the
> proof which did not look at all a routine job. When
> you have satisfied yourself that the theorem is **true,**
> you start **proving** it. (emphasis added)

In situations like the above where conviction prior to proof provides the motivation for a proof, the function of the proof clearly must be something other than verification/conviction.

In real mathematical research, personal conviction usually depends on a combination of intuition, quasi-empirical verification, and the existence of a logical (but not necessarily rigorous) proof. In fact, a very high level of conviction may sometimes be reached even in the absence of a proof. For instance, in their discussion of the "heuristic evidence" in support of the still unproved twin prime pair theorem and the famous Riemann Hypothesis, Davis and Hersh (1983, 369) conclude that this evidence is "so strong that it carries conviction even without rigorous proof."

That conviction for mathematicians is not reached by proof alone is also strikingly borne out by the remark of a previous editor of *Mathematical Reviews* that approximately one half of the proofs published in it were incomplete and/or contained errors, although the theorems they were purported to prove were essentially true (Hanna 1983, 71). Research mathematicians, for instance, seldom scrutinize the published proofs of results in detail, but are led, rather, by the established authority of the author, the testing of special cases, and an informal evaluation whether *"the methods and result fit in, seem reasonable. . ."* (Davis and Hersh 1986, 67). Also according to Hanna (1989) the reasonableness of results often enjoy priority over the existence of a completely rigorous proof.

When investigating the validity of a new, unknown conjecture, mathematicians usually do not only look for proofs, but also try to construct counterexamples at the same time by means of quasi-empirical testing, since such testing may expose hidden contradictions, errors, or unsaid assumptions. In this way, counterexamples are sometimes produced, requiring mathematicians to reconstruct old proofs and construct new ones. In attaining conviction, the failure to disprove conjectures empirically plays just as important a role as the process of deductive justification. It appears that there is a logical, as well as a psychological, dimension to attaining certainty. Logically, we require some form of deductive proof, but psychologically it seems we need some experimental exploration or intuitive understanding as well.

Of course, in view of the well-known limitations of intuition and quasi-empirical methods themselves, the preceding arguments are definitely not meant to disregard the importance of proof as an indispensable means of verification, especially in the case of surprising non-intuitive or doubtful results. Rather it is intended to place a more proper perspective on proof as opposed to a distorted idolization of proof as the only (and absolute) means of verification/conviction.

## PROOF AS A MEANS OF EXPLANATION

Although it is possible to achieve quite a high level of confidence in the validity of a conjecture by means of quasi-empirical verification (for example, accurate constructions and measurement, numerical substitution, and so on), this generally provides no satisfactory explanation why the conjecture may be true. It merely confirms that it is true, and even though considering more and more examples may increase one's confidence even more, it gives no psychologically satisfactory sense of illumination—no insight or understanding into how the conjecture is the consequence of other familiar results. For instance, despite the convincing heuristic evidence in support of the earlier mentioned Riemann Hypothesis, one may still have a burning need for explanation as stated by Davis and Hersh (1983, 368):

> It is interesting to ask, in a context such as this, why we still feel the need for a proof . . . It seems clear that we want a proof because . . . if something is true and we can't deduce it in this way, this is a sign of a lack of understanding on our part. We believe, in other words, that a proof would be a way of understanding why the Riemann conjecture is true, which is something more than just knowing from convincing heuristic reasoning that it **is** true.

Gale (1990, 4) also clearly emphasizes as follows, with reference to Feigenbaum's experimental discoveries in fractal geometry, that the function of their eventual proofs was that of explanation and not that of verification at all:

> Lanford and other mathematicians were not trying to validate Feigenbaum's results any more than, say, Newton was trying to **validate** the discoveries of Kepler on the planetary orbits. In both cases the validity of the results was never in question. What was missing was the **explanation.** Why were the orbits ellipses? Why did they satisfy these particular relations? . . . there's a world of difference between validating and explaining. (emphasis added)

Thus, in most cases when the results concerned are intuitively self-evident and/or they are supported by convincing quasi-empirical evidence, the function of proof for mathematicians is not that of verification, but rather that of explanation (or the other functions of proof described further on).

In fact, for many mathematicians the clarification/explanation aspect of a proof is of greater importance than the aspect of verification. For instance, the well-known Paul Halmos stated some time ago that although the computer-assisted proof of the four color theorem by Appel and Haken convinced him that it was true, he would still personally prefer a proof that also gives an "understanding" (Albers 1982, 239–240). Manin (1981, 107) and Bell (1976, 24) also believed that explanation is a criterion for a "good" proof when stating respectively that it is "one which makes us wiser" and that it is expected "to convey an insight into why the proposition is true."

## PROOF AS A MEANS OF DISCOVERY

It is often said that theorems are most often first discovered by means of intuition and/or quasi-empirical methods, before they are verified by the production of proofs. However, there are numerous examples in the history of mathematics where new results were discovered or invented in a purely deductive manner; in fact, it is completely unlikely that some results (for example, the non-Euclidean geometries) could ever have been chanced upon merely by intuition and/or only using quasi-empirical methods. Even within the context of such formal deductive processes as axiomatization and defining, proof can frequently lead to new results. To the working mathematician, proof is therefore not merely a means of verifying an already-discovered result, but often also a means of exploring, analyzing, discovering, and inventing new results (compare Schoenfeld 1986 and de Jager 1990).

For instance, consider the following example. Suppose we have constructed a dynamic kite with Sketchpad and connected the midpoints of the sides to form a quadrilateral *EFGH* as shown below. Visually, *EFGH* clearly appears to be a rectangle, which can easily be confirmed by measuring the angles. By grabbing any vertex of the kite *ABCD*, we could now drag it to a new position to verify that *EFGH* remains a rectangle. We could also drag vertex *A* downward until *ABCD* becomes concave to check whether it remains true. Although such continuous variation can easily convince us, it provides no satisfactory explanation why the midpoint quadrilateral of a kite is a rectangle. However, if we produce a deductive proof for this conjecture, we immediately notice that the perpendicularity of the diagonals is the essential characteristic upon which it depends, and that the property of equal adjacent sides is therefore not required. (The proof is left to the reader.)

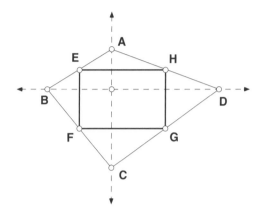

In other words, we can immediately generalize the result to any quadrilateral with perpendicular diagonals (a perpendicular quadrilateral) as shown by the figure above. In contrast, the general result is not at all suggested by the purely empirical verification of the original hypothesis. Even a systematic empirical investigation of various types of quadrilaterals would probably not have helped to discover the general case, since we would probably have restricted our investigation to the familiar quadrilaterals such as parallelograms, rectangles, rhombuses, squares, and isosceles trapezoids.

The Theorem of Ceva (1678) was probably discovered in a similar deductive fashion by generalizing from a proof for the concurrency of the medians of a triangle, and not by actual construction and measurement (see de Villiers, 1988). However, new results can also be discovered *a priori* by simply deductively analyzing the properties of given objects. For example, without resorting to actual construction and measurement it is possible to quickly deduce that $AB + CD = BC + DA$ for the quadrilateral *ABCD* circumscribed around a circle, as shown below by using the theorem that the tangents from a point outside a circle to the circle are equal.

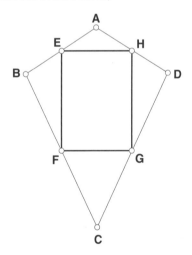

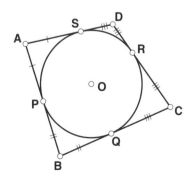

Rethinking Proof
© 2003 Key Curriculum Press

## PROOF AS A MEANS OF SYSTEMATIZATION

Proof exposes the underlying logical relationships between statements in ways no amount of quasi-empirical testing nor pure intuition can. Proof is therefore an indispensable tool for systematizing various known results into a deductive system of axioms, definitions, and theorems. Some of the most important functions of a deductive systematization of known results are given as follows by de Villiers (1986):

- It helps identify inconsistencies, circular arguments, and hidden, or not explicitly stated, assumptions.

- It unifies and simplifies mathematical theories by integrating unrelated statements, theorems, and concepts with one another, thus leading to an economical presentation of results.

- It provides a useful global perspective or bird's-eye view of a topic by exposing the underlying axiomatic structure of that topic from which all the other properties may be derived.

- It is helpful for applications both within and outside mathematics, since it makes it possible to check the applicability of a whole complex structure or theory by simply evaluating the suitability of its axioms and definitions.

- It often leads to alternative deductive systems that provide new perspectives and/or are more economical, elegant, and powerful than existing ones.

Although some elements of verification are obviously also present here, the main objective clearly is not "to check whether certain statements are really true," but to organize logically unrelated individual statements that are already known to be true into *a coherent unified whole*. Due to the global perspective provided by such simplification and unification, there is of course also a distinct element of illumination present when proof is used as a means of systematization. In this case, however, the focus falls on

global rather than local illumination. Thus, it is in reality false to say, when proving self-evident statements such as that the opposite angles of two intersecting lines are equal, that we are "making sure." Mathematicians are actually far less concerned about the truth of such theorems than with their systematization into a deductive system.

## PROOF AS A MEANS OF COMMUNICATION

Several authors have stressed the importance of the communicative function of proof, for example:

> . . . *it appears that proof is a form of **discourse**, a means of communication among people doing mathematics.* (Volmink 1990, 8; emphasis added)

> . . . *we recognize that mathematical argument is addressed to a human audience, which possesses a background knowledge enabling it to understand the intentions of the speaker or author. In stating that mathematical argument is not mechanical or formal, we have also stated implicitly what it is . . . namely, a **human interchange** based on shared meanings, not all of which are verbal or formulaic.* (Davis and Hersh 1986, 73; emphasis added)

Similarly, Davis (1976) has also mentioned that one of the real values of proof is that it creates a forum for critical debate. According to this view, proof is a unique way of communicating mathematical results between professional mathematicians, between teachers and students, and among students themselves. The emphasis thus falls on the social process of reporting and disseminating mathematical knowledge in society. Proof as a form of social interaction therefore also involves subjectively negotiating not only of concepts concerned, but implicitly also the criteria for an acceptable argument. In turn, such a social filtration of a proof in various communications contributes to its refinement and the identification of errors, as well as sometimes to its rejection by the discovery of a counterexample.

## PROOF AS A MEANS OF INTELLECTUAL CHALLENGE

To mathematicians, proof is an *intellectual challenge* that they find as appealing as other people find puzzles or creative hobbies or endeavors. Most people have sufficient experience, if only in attempting to solve a crossword or jigzaw puzzle, to enable them to understand the exuberance with which Pythagoras and Archimedes are said to have celebrated the discovery of their proofs. Doing proofs could also be compared to the physical challenge of completing an arduous marathon or triathlon, and the satisfaction that comes afterward. In this sense, the intellectual challenge function of proof results in self-realization and fulfillment. Proof is therefore a testing ground for the intellectual stamina and ingenuity of the mathematician (compare Davis and Hersh 1983, 369). To paraphrase George Mallory's famous comment on his reason for climbing Mount Everest: *We prove our results because they're there.* Pushing this analogy even further: It is often not the existence of the mountain that is in doubt (the truth of the result), but whether (and how) one can conquer (prove) it!

Finally, although the six functions of proof can be distinguished from one another, they are often all interwoven in specific cases. In some cases certain functions may dominate others, while in other cases certain functions may not feature at all. Furthermore, this list of functions is by no means complete. For instance, we could easily add an *aesthetic* function or that of *memorization* and algorithm development (Renz 1981 and van Asch 1993).

## TEACHING PROOF WITH SKETCHPAD

When students have thoroughly investigated a geometric conjecture through continuous variation with dynamic software like Sketchpad, they have little need for further conviction or verification. So verification serves as little or no motivation for doing a proof. However, I have found it relatively easy to solicit further curiosity by asking students *why* they think a particular result is true; that is, to challenge them to try and *explain* it. Students quickly admit that inductive verification merely confirms; it gives no

satisfactory sense of illumination, insight, or understanding into how the conjecture is a consequence of other familiar results. Students therefore find it quite satisfactory to then view a deductive argument as an attempt at explanation, rather than verification.

It is also advisable to introduce students early on to the discovery function of proof and to give attention to the communicative aspects throughout by negotiating and clarifying with your students the criteria for acceptable evidence, the underlying heuristics and logic of proof. The verification function of proof should be reserved for results where students genuinely exhibit doubts. Although some students may not experience proof as an intellectual challenge for themselves, they are able to appreciate that others can experience it in this way. Furthermore, in real mathematics, as anyone with a bit of experience will testify, the purely systematization function of proof comes to the fore only at an advanced stage and should therefore be withheld in an introductory course to proof. It seems meaningful to initially introduce students to the various functions of proof more or less in the sequence given above, although not in purely linear fashion as shown, but in a kind of spiral approach where other earlier introduced functions are revisited and expanded. The chapters of this book are organized according to this sequence, and a few approaches to spiraling through the sequence are suggested in the Introduction.

## THE VAN HIELE THEORY

The van Hiele theory originated in the doctoral dissertations of Dina van Hiele-Geldof and her husband Pierre van Hiele at the University of Utrecht, Netherlands, in 1957. While Pierre's dissertation mainly tried to explain why students experienced problems in geometry education (in this respect it was *explanatory* and *descriptive*), Dina's dissertation was about a teaching experiment (in this sense more *prescriptive* regarding the ordering of geometry content and learning activities of students). The most obvious characteristic of the theory is the distinction of five discrete thought levels in the development of students' understanding of geometry.

According to the van Hiele theory, the main reason traditional geometry curriculum fails is that it is presented at a higher level than those at which students are operating; in other words, students cannot understand the teacher nor can the teacher understand why they cannot understand! Although the van Hiele theory distinguishes between five different levels of thought, we shall only focus on the first four levels, as they are the most pertinent ones for secondary school geometry. The general characteristics of the first four levels are described here.

## Level 1: Recognition

Students visually recognize figures by their global appearance. They recognize triangles, squares, parallelograms, and so forth by their shape, but they do not explicitly identify the properties of these figures.

## Level 2: Analysis

Students start analyzing the properties of figures and learn the appropriate technical terminology for describing them, but they do not interrelate figures or properties of figures.

## Level 3: Ordering

Students logically order the properties of figures by short chains of deductions and understand the interrelationships between figures (for example, class inclusions).

## Level 4: Deduction

Students start developing longer sequences of statements and begin to understand the significance of deduction, the role of axioms, theorems, and proof.

The differences between the first three levels can be summarized as shown in the table below in terms of the objects and structure of thought at each level (see Fuys et al., 1988, 6)

|  | Level 1 | Level 2 | Level 3 |
|---|---|---|---|
| **Objects of thought** | Individual figures | Classes of figures | Definitions of classes of figures |
| **Structure of thought** | Visual recognition Naming Visual sorting | Recognizing properties as characteristics of classes | Noticing and formulating logical relationships between properties |
| **Examples** | Parallelograms all go together because they *"look the same."* Rectangles, squares, and rhombuses are not parallelograms because they do *"not look like one."* | A parallelogram has four sides, opposite angles equal, opposite sides equal, opposite sides parallel, bisecting diagonals, and so on. A rectangle is not a parallelogram since a rectangle has 90° angles but a parallelogram does not. | Opposite sides equal imply opposite sides parallel. Opposite sides parallel imply opposite sides equal. Opposite angles equal imply opposite sides equal. Bisecting diagonals imply half-turn symmetry. |

By using task-based interviews, Burger and Shaughnessy (1986) identified what students do at the first four levels more fully as follows:

## Level 1

1. Often use irrelevant visual properties to identify figures, to compare, to classify, and to describe.

2. Usually refer to visual prototypes of figures, and are easily misled by the orientation of figures.

3. Are unable to think of an infinite variation of a particular type of figure; for example, in terms of orientation and shape.

4. Inconsistently classify figures; for example, use non-common or irrelevant properties to sort figures.

5. Incompletely describe (define) figures by viewing necessary (often visual) conditions as sufficient conditions.

## Level 2

1. Make an explicit comparison of figures in terms of their underlying properties.

2. Avoid class inclusions between different classes of figures; for example, squares and rectangles are considered to be disjoint.

3. Sort figures only in terms of one property; for example, properties of sides, while other properties like symmetries, angles, and diagonals are ignored.

4. Exhibit an uneconomical use of the properties of figures to describe (define) them, instead of just using sufficient properties.

5. Explicitly reject definitions supplied by other people; for example, a teacher or textbook, in favor of their own personal definitions.

6. Approach the establishment of the truth of a statement empirically; for example, use observation and measurement on the basis of several sketches.

## Level 3

1. Formulate economical, correct definitions for figures.

2. Are able to transform incomplete definitions into complete definitions and more spontaneously accept and use definitions for new concepts.

3. Accept different equivalent definitions for the same concept.

4. Classify figures hierarchically; for example, quadrilaterals.

5. Explicitly use the logical form *if . . . then* to formulate and handle conjectures, and implicitly use logical rules such as *modus ponens*.

6. Are uncertain and lack understanding regarding the functions of axioms, definitions, and proof.

## Level 4

1. Understand the functions (roles) of axioms, definitions, and proof.

2. Spontaneously make conjectures and self-initiate efforts to deductively verify them.

According to the van Hiele theory, deductive reasoning first occurs on Level 3, when the network of logical relationships between properties is established. In other words, when a proof for the equality of the diagonals of a rectangle is developed, the meaning of such a proof lies in making the logical relationships between the properties explicit. A student at Level 1 or 2, who does not yet possess this network of logical implications, can only experience such a proof as an attempt at the verification of the result. However, since such students do not doubt the validity of their empirical observations, they tend to experience it as meaningless, or "proving the obvious." It should further be noted that the transition from van Hiele Level 1 to Level 2 poses specific problems to second language learners, since it involves acquiring technical terminology for describing properties of figures.

## CONCEPTUAL STRUCTURING

An important aspect of the van Hiele theory is that it emphasizes that informal activities at Levels 1 and 2 should provide appropriate *conceptual substructures* for the formal activities at the next level. Teachers often let their students measure the angles of a triangle with a protractor, and then let them add the angles to discover that they always add up to 180°. From a van Hiele perspective this is inappropriate as it does not provide a suitable conceptual substructure in which the eventual logical explanation (proof) is implicitly embedded. In comparison, an activity with cardboard tiles, or Sketchpad as shown below, provides such a substructure. For example, translate a triangle *ABC* by vector *BC,* and rotate triangle *ABC* around the midpoint of *AC.* Let the students notice through dragging that the three angles *C, D,* and *E* always form a straight line. Then ask students what they can say about angles *A* and *B* in relation to angles *D* and *E.* Since angle *B* maps onto angle *E* by the translation, and angle *A* maps onto angle *D* by the half-turn, angles *B* and *A* are equal to angles *D* and *E,* respectively. Clearly this provides an appropriate conceptual structure for an eventual explanation (proof).

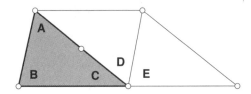

Similarly, the activity of measuring the base angles of an isosceles triangle and dragging the triangle within Sketchpad is conceptually inappropriate, but reflecting it around its axis of symmetry lays the foundation for a logical explanation (proof) later.

## THE RECONSTRUCTIVE APPROACH

Early in this century the German mathematician Felix Klein (1924) came out strongly against the practice of presenting mathematical topics as completed axiomatic-deductive systems and instead argued for the use of the so-called *bio-genetic* principle in teaching. The genetic approach has also been advocated by Wittmann (1973), Polya (1981), Freudenthal (1973), and many others. Essentially, the genetic approach argues that the learner should either retrace (at least in part) the path followed by the original discoverers or inventors, or retrace a path by which mathematical content could have been discovered or invented. In other words, learners should be exposed to or engaged with the typical mathematical processes by which new content in mathematics is discovered, invented, and organized. Human (1978, 20) calls it the *reconstructive* approach and contrasts it as follows with the so-called *direct axiomatic-deductive* approach:

> *With this term we want to indicate that content is not directly introduced to students (as finished products of mathematical activity), but that the content is newly reconstructed during teaching in a typical mathematical manner by the teacher and/or the students.* (translation mine)

The didactical motivation for the reconstructive approach includes, among others, the following two elements: that it highlights the *meaning* of the content, and that it allows students to *actively participate* in constructing and developing the content. In recent times, the learning theory of constructivism has provided a psychological perspective which strongly supports such a teaching approach. With different content (definitions, axiom systems, propositions, proofs, algorithms, and so on) one can of course distinguish different mathematical processes for constructing that content. A genetic or reconstructive approach is therefore characterized by not presenting content as a finished, prefabricated product, but rather focusing on the genuine mathematical processes by which the content can be developed or reconstructed. Note, however, that a reconstructive approach does not necessarily imply learning by discovery, for it may just be a reconstructive explanation by the teacher or the textbook. It also does not mean that a historical approach need be strictly followed, but simply that the history of mathematics serves as useful guide.

## DEFINING

> *The intrinsic value of mathematics is not only contained in the* products *of mathematical activity (i.e. polished concepts, definitions, structures and axiomatic systems, but also and especially in the processes of mathematical activity leading to such products, e.g. generalization, recognition of pattern,*

*defining, axiomatizing. The draft syllabi are intended to reflect an increased emphasis on genuine mathematical activity as opposed to the mere assimilation of the finished products of such activity. This emphasis is particularly reflected in the various sections on geometry.* (Mathematical Association of South Africa 1978, 3)

Traditionally most teachers and textbook authors have simply provided students with ready-made content (definitions, theorems, proofs, classifications, and so on) that they merely have to assimilate and regurgitate in tests and exams. Traditional geometry education of this kind can be compared to a cooking class where the teacher only shows students cakes (or even worse, only pictures of cakes) without showing them what goes into the cake and how it is made. In addition, they're not even allowed to try their own hand at baking!

The direct teaching of geometry definitions with no emphasis on the underlying process of defining has often been criticized by mathematicians and mathematics educators alike. For example, as early as 1908, Benchara Blandford wrote (quoted in Griffiths and Howson 1974, 216–217):

*To me it appears a radically vicious method, certainly in geometry, if not in other subjects, to supply a child with ready-made definitions, to be subsequently memorized after being more or less carefully explained. To do this is surely to throw away deliberately one of the most valuable agents of intellectual discipline. The evolving of a workable definition by the child's own activity stimulated by appropriate questions, is both interesting and highly educational. Let us try to discover the kind of conception already existing in the child's mind— vague and crude it generally is, of course, otherwise what need for education?—let us note carefully its defects, and then help the child himself to refashion the conception . . .*

The well-known mathematician Hans Freudenthal (1973, 416–418) also strongly criticized the traditional practice of the direct provision of geometry definitions as follows:

*. . . the Socratic didactician would refuse to introduce the geometrical objects by definitions, but wherever the didactic inversion prevails, deductivity starts with definitions. (In traditional geometry they even define what is a definition—a still higher level in the learning process.) The Socratic didactician rejects such a procedure. How can you define a thing before you know what you have to define?. . . most definitions are not preconceived but the finishing touch of the organizing activity. The child should not be deprived of this privilege . . . Good geometry instruction can mean much—learning to organize a subject matter and learning what is organizing, learning to conceptualize and what is conceptualizing, learning to define and what is a definition. It means leading pupils to understand why some organization, some concept, some definition is better than another. Traditional instruction is different. Rather than giving the child the opportunity to organize spatial experiences, the subject matter is offered as a preorganized structure. All concepts, definitions, and deductions are preconceived by the teacher, who knows what is its use in every detail—or rather by the textbook author who has carefully built all his secrets into the structure.*

Just knowing the definition of a concept does not at all guarantee understanding of the concept. For example, although students may have been taught, and be able to recite, the standard definition of a parallelogram as a quadrilateral with opposite sides parallel, the students may still not consider rectangles, squares, and rhombuses as parallelograms, since the students' concept image of a parallelogram is that not all angles or sides are allowed to be equal. It would appear that in order to increase students' understanding of geometry definitions, and of the concepts to which they relate, it is essential to engage students at some stage in the process of defining geometric concepts. Due to the inherent complexity of the process of defining, it would also appear to be unreasonable to expect students to immediately come up with formal definitions on their own, unless they have been guided in a didactic fashion through some examples of the process of defining that they can later use as models for their own attempts.

Furthermore, constructing definitions is a mathematical activity of no less importance than other mathematical processes such as solving problems, making conjectures, generalizing, specializing, proving, and so on, and it is therefore strange that it has been neglected in most mathematics teaching. In mathematics we can distinguish between two different types of defining of concepts, namely, *descriptive (a posteriori)* and *constructive (a priori)* defining (for example, compare Krygowska 1971; Human 1978, 164–65; de Villiers 1998b).

### Descriptive Defining

> *. . . the describing definition . . . outlines a known object by singling out a few characteristic properties.* (Freudenthal 1973, 458)

Descriptive defining occurs after a concept and its properties have already been known for some time (see below). Descriptive defining is usually accomplished by selecting an appropriate subset of the total set of properties of the concept from which all the other properties can be deduced. This subset then serves as the definition and the other remaining properties are then logically derived from it as theorems.

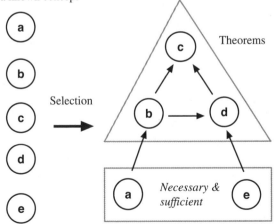

### Constructive Defining

> *. . . the algorithmically constructive and creative definition . . . models new objects out of familiar ones.* (Freudenthal 1973, 458)

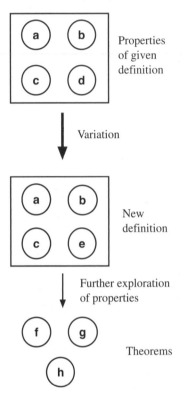

Constructive defining is done by changing a given definition by excluding, generalizing, specializing, replacing, or adding properties to the definition, so that a new concept is constructed in the process (see above). In other words, a new concept is defined *into being*, and its further properties can then be experimentally or logically explored. Whereas the main purpose or function of descriptive defining is to *systematize* existing knowledge, the main function of constructive defining is to produce *new* knowledge.

From our preceding discussion of the van Hiele theory it should be clear that understanding of formal, textbook definitions only develops at Level 3 and that the direct provision of such definitions to students at lower levels would be doomed to failure. In fact, if we take the constructivist theory of learning seriously (namely that knowledge simply cannot be transferred directly from one person to another and that meaningful knowledge needs to be actively constructed by the learner), we should actually engage students in the activity of defining and allow them to choose their own definitions at each level. For example, to define a rectangle, this implies allowing the following kinds of meaningful definitions at each van Hiele level:

**van Hiele Level 1**

*Visual* definitions; for example, a rectangle that looks like this (draws or identifies a quadrilateral with all angles 90° and two long and two short sides).

**van Hiele Level 2**

*Uneconomical* definitions; for example, a rectangle is a quadrilateral with opposite sides parallel and equal, all angles 90°, equal diagonals, half-turn-symmetry, two axes of symmetry through opposite sides, two long and two short sides, and so on.

**van Hiele Level 3**

*Correct, economical* definitions; for example, a rectangle is a quadrilateral with two axes of symmetry though opposite sides.

## HIERARCHICAL VERSUS PARTITIONAL DEFINITIONS

As you can see above from the two examples at van Hiele Levels 1 and 2, students' spontaneous definitions would also tend to be *partitional,* in other words, they would not allow the inclusion of the squares among the rectangles (by explicitly stating two long and two short sides). In contrast, according to the van Hiele theory, definitions at Level 3 are typically hierarchical, which means they allow for the inclusion of the squares among the rectangles, and would not be understood by students at lower levels.

Formal definitions in textbooks are often preceded by an activity whereby students have to compare in tabular form various properties of the quadrilaterals, for example, to see that a square, rectangle, and rhombus have all the properties of a parallelogram. The purpose clearly is to prepare them for the formal definitions later on which are hierarchical. (In other words, the given definitions provide for the inclusion of special cases; for example, a parallelogram is defined so as to include squares, rhombuses, and rectangles.) However, research reported in de Villiers (1994) shows that many students, even after

doing tabular comparisons and other activities, if given the opportunity, still prefer to define quadrilaterals in partitions. (In other words, they would, for example, still prefer to define a parallelogram as a quadrilateral with both pairs of opposite sides parallel, but not all angles or sides equal.)

For this reason, students should not simply be supplied with ready-made definitions for the quadrilaterals, but should be allowed to formulate their own definitions irrespective of whether they are partitional or hierarchical. By then discussing and comparing in class the relative advantages and disadvantages of these two different ways of classifying and defining quadrilaterals (both of which are mathematically correct), students may be led to realize that there are certain advantages in accepting a hierarchical classification. For example, if students are asked to compare the following two definitions for parallelogram, they might realize that the former is more economical than the latter:

Hierarchical:  A parallelogram is a quadrilateral with both pairs of opposite sides parallel.

Partitional:  A parallelogram is a quadrilateral with both pairs of opposite sides parallel, but not all angles or sides equal.

Clearly, in general, partitional definitions are longer since they have to include additional properties to ensure the exclusion of special cases. Another advantage of a hierarchical definition for a concept is that all theorems proved for that concept then apply automatically to its special cases. For example, if we prove that the diagonals of a parallelogram bisect each other, we can immediately conclude that it is also true for rectangles, rhombuses, and squares. If, however, we classified and defined them partitionally, we would have to prove separately in each case, for parallelograms, rectangles, rhombuses, and squares, that their diagonals bisect each other. Clearly this is very uneconomical. It seems clear that unless the role and function of a hierarchical classification is meaningfully discussed in class as described in de Villiers (1994), many students will have difficulty in understanding why their intuitive, partitional definitions are not used.

On the other hand, the dynamic nature of geometric figures constructed in Sketchpad may also make the acceptance of a hierarchical classification of the quadrilaterals far easier. For example, if students construct a quadrilateral with opposite sides parallel, then they will notice that they could easily drag it into the shape of a rectangle, rhombus, or square as shown below. In fact, it seems quite possible that students would be able to accept and understand this even at van Hiele Level 1 (visualization), but further research into this particular area is needed.

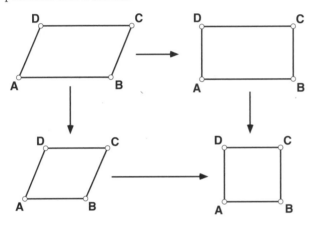

Dynamic transformation of parallelogram

## CONSTRUCTION AND MEASUREMENT

It should first be pointed out that certain kinds of construction activities (on Sketchpad or by pencil and paper) are inappropriate at van Hiele Level 1. For example, someone was recently overheard at a conference commenting that she was unpleasantly dismayed at the difficulty young children had with the task of constructing a "dynamic" square with Sketchpad. However, if the children were still at van Hiele Level 1, then it is not surprising at all—how can they construct it if they do not yet know its properties (Level 2) and that some properties are sufficient and others not (that is, know the logical relationships between the properties—Level 3)?

In fact, at van Hiele Level 1 it would appear to be far more appropriate to provide children with ready-made sketches of quadrilaterals in Sketchpad, which they can then easily manipulate and first investigate visually. Next, they could start using the measure features of the software to analyze the properties (and learn the appropriate terminology) to enable them to reach Level 2. Only then would it be appropriate to challenge them to construct such dynamic

quadrilaterals themselves, thus assisting the transition to Level 3.

In other words, students who are predominantly at van Hiele Level 2 cannot yet be expected to logically check their own descriptions (definitions) of quadrilaterals, but they should be allowed to do so by accurate construction and measurement. For example, students could evaluate the following attempted descriptions (definitions) for a rhombus by construction and measurement as shown in the figure below:

1. A rhombus is a quadrilateral with all sides equal.

2. A rhombus is a quadrilateral with perpendicular, bisecting diagonals.

3. A rhombus is a quadrilateral with bisecting diagonals.

4. A rhombus is a quadrilateral with one pair of adjacent sides equal and both pairs of opposite sides parallel.

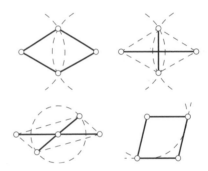

Construction and measurement

In the first example, students should construct a quadrilateral so that all four sides are equal, and then could notice that the diagonals always bisect each other perpendicularly, irrespective of how they drag the figure. This clearly shows that the property of "perpendicular bisecting diagonals" is a consequence of their constructing "all four sides equal." On the other hand, such testing also clearly shows when a description (definition) is incomplete (contains insufficient properties), as in the third example above.

Psychologically, constructions like these are extremely important for assisting the transition from van Hiele Level 2 to van Hiele Level 3. It helps to develop an understanding of the difference between a *premise* and a *conclusion* and

© 2003 Key Curriculum Press

their causal relationship; in other words, of the logical structure of an *if-then* statement. For example, statement 4 could be rewritten by students as: "*If* a quadrilateral has one pair of adjacent sides equal and both pairs of opposite sides parallel, *then* it is a rhombus (that is, has all sides equal, perpendicular bisecting diagonals, and so on)." Smith (1940) reported marked improvement in students' understanding of *if-then* statements after letting them make constructions to evaluate geometric statements as follows:

> *Pupils saw that when they did certain things in making a figure, certain other things resulted. They learned to feel the difference in category between the relationships they **put** into a figure—the things over which they had control—and the relationships which **resulted** without any action on their part. Finally the difference in these two categories was associated with the difference between the **given** conditions and **conclusion,** between the if-part and the then-part of a sentence.* (emphasis added)

## PHASES IN GEOMETRY EDUCATION

According to the van Hiele theory, for learning to be meaningful, students should become acquainted that, and explore, geometry content in phases that correspond to the van Hiele levels. A serious shortcoming of the van Hiele theory, however, is that there is no explicit distinction between different possible functions of proof. For example, the development of deductive thinking appears first within the context of *systematization* at van Hiele Level 3 (ordering). Empirical research by de Villiers (1991) and Mudaly (1998) seem to indicate, however, that the functions of proof such as *explanation, discovery,* and *verification* can be meaningful to students outside a systematization context, in other words, at van Hiele levels lower than van Hiele Level 3, provided the arguments are of an intuitive or visual nature; for example, the use of symmetry or dissection. From experience, it also seems that a prolonged delay at van Hiele levels 1 and 2 before introducing proof actually makes introducing proof later as a meaningful activity even more difficult. The following are four example activities sequenced to not only correspond to the van Hiele levels, but also to incorporate a distinction between some different functions of proof at these levels.

## Activity 1: Exploration of Properties of a Kite

In this activity students use Sketchpad to first construct a kite by using reflection and then explore its properties (for example, angles, sides, diagonals, circum circle). By dragging, students also explore special cases (rhombus, square).

This activity

- Involves van Hiele Level 1 (visualization) and van Hiele Level 2 (analysis and formulation of properties)
- Asks students to *explain* (prove) properties of kites in terms of reflective symmetry

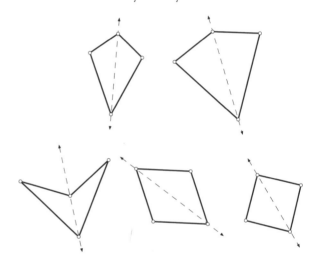

**Construct**

1. Draw a line through two points, and then construct any point not on the line.

2. Reflect the "outside" point in the line.

3. Connect corresponding points to obtain a quadrilateral as shown above.

**Investigate**

1. Make conjectures regarding the following properties of the above figures:
   a. sides      b. angles
   c. diagonals      d. inscribed or circumscribed circle

2. Can the above figure sometimes be a parallelogram, rectangle, rhombus, or square?

3. Logically explain your conjectures in Question 1 in terms of symmetry.

## Activity 2: Constructing the Midpoints of the Sides of a Kite

Students construct the midpoints of the sides of a dynamic kite and explore the kind of figure formed (leading to the conjecture that it is a rectangle).

This activity

- Explains that midpoints form a rectangle in terms of perpendicularity of diagonals, leading to the *discovery* that this would be true for any quadrilateral with perpendicular diagonals

### Construct

Construct and connect the midpoints of the sides of a kite.

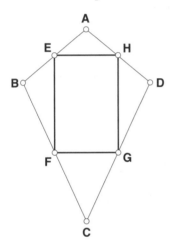

### Investigate

1. Investigate the type of quadrilateral formed by the midpoints of its sides.

2. Logically explain your conjecture.

3. From Question 2, can you find or construct another more general type of quadrilateral that will have the same midpoint property? (The result generalizes to any quadrilateral with perpendicular diagonals.)

## Activity 3: Describing a Kite

Students select different subsets of the properties of a kite as possible descriptions (definitions) and first check whether they are necessary and sufficient by using them in a Sketchpad construction, and then by logical reasoning (proof).

This activity

- Involves van Hiele Level 3 (local ordering)

- Makes explicit the function of proof as *systematization* (that is, the deductive organization of the properties of a kite)

- Involves the mathematical process of *descriptive* defining

The kite has the following properties:

   a. (At least) one line of symmetry through a pair of opposite angles

   b. Perpendicular diagonals (with at least one bisecting the other)

   c. (At least) one pair of opposite angles equal

   d. Two (distinct) pairs of adjacent sides equal

   e. (At least) one diagonal bisecting a pair of opposite angles

   f. Incircle

### Investigate

1. How would you over the phone explain what "kites" are to someone not yet acquainted with them? (Try to keep your description as short as possible, but ensure that the person has enough information to make a correct drawing of the quadrilateral).

2. Try formulating two alternative descriptions. Which of the three do you like best? Why?

## Activity 4: Generalizing or Specializing a Kite

Students generalize by leaving out some of the properties and specialize by adding more properties. The properties of the newly defined objects are then explored by construction on Sketchpad and/or by deductive reasoning.

This activity

- Involves van Hiele Level 4 (global ordering)
- Involves the mathematical process of constructive defining

**Investigate**

1. Generalize the concept "kite" in different ways by leaving out, altering, or generalizing some of its properties. (One possibility is to generalize to a $2n$-gon; for example, a polygon with at least one axis of symmetry through a pair of opposite angles. Other possibilities are to generalize to a quadrilateral with at least one pair of adjacent sides equal, to one with one diagonal bisected by the other, or to one circumscribed around a circle—a circum quad).

2. Specialize the concept "kite" in different ways by the addition of more properties. (Possibilities to consider are a kite inscribed in a circle, a kite with at least three equal angles, or a kite with another axis of symmetry through a pair of opposite angles—a rhombus).

These briefly described activities are intended as examples of how students can be engaged in proof at levels lower than van Hiele Level 3. The more fully developed activities in this book resemble these four activities in structure and are likewise intended to engage students operating at various van Hiele levels. I hope they illustrate that the van Hiele theory does not so much require us to avoid proof as it requires us to engage students in proof's various functions.

# Proof as

Explanation

A shipwreck survivor manages to swim to a desert island. As it happens, the island closely approximates the shape of an equilateral triangle. She soon discovers that the surfing is outstanding on all three of the island's coasts. She crafts a surfboard from a fallen tree and surfs every day. Where should she build her house so that the sum of the distances from her house to all three beaches is as small as possible? (She visits each beach with equal frequency.) Before you proceed further, locate a point in the triangle at the spot where you think she should build her house.

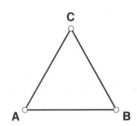

## CONJECTURE

☞ Open the sketch **Distances.gsp.** Drag point *P* to experiment with your sketch.

1. Press the button to show the distance sum. Drag point *P* around the interior of the triangle. What do you notice about the sum of the distances?

2. Drag a vertex of the triangle to change the triangle's size. Again, drag point *P* around the interior of the triangle. What do you notice now?

3. What happens if you drag *P* outside the triangle?

4. Organize your observations from Questions 1–3 into a conjecture. Write your conjecture using complete sentences.

## EXPLAINING

You are no doubt convinced that the total sum of the distances from point *P* to all three sides of a given equilateral triangle is always constant, as long as *P* is an interior point. But can you explain *why* this is true?

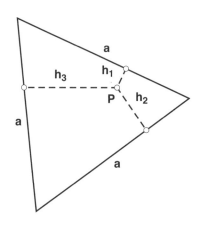

$$h_2 + h_3 + h_1 = 4.46 \text{ cm}$$

Although further exploration in Sketchpad might succeed in convincing you even more fully of the truth of your conjecture, it would only confirm the conjecture's truth without providing an explanation. For example, the observation that the sun rises every morning does not explain why this is true. We have to try to explain it in terms of something else, for example, the rotation of the earth around the polar axis.

Recently, a mathematician named Mitchell Feigenbaum made some experimental discoveries in fractal geometry using a computer, just as you have used Sketchpad to discover your conjecture about a point inside an equilateral triangle. Feigenbaum's discoveries were later explained by Oscar Lanford and others. Here's what another mathematician had to say about all this:

> *Lanford and other mathematicians were not trying to validate Feigenbaum's results any more than, say, Newton was trying to validate the discoveries of Kepler on the planetary orbits. In both cases the validity of the results was never in question. What was missing was the explanation. Why were the orbits ellipses? Why did they satisfy these particular relations? . . . there's a world of difference between validating and explaining.*
>
> —*M. D. Gale, 1990*

**CHALLENGE**    Use another sheet of paper to try to logically explain your conjecture from Question 4. After you have thought for a while and made some notes, use the steps and questions that follow to develop an explanation of your conjectures.

👉 Press the button to show the small triangles in your sketch.

5. Drag a vertex of the original triangle. Why are the three different sides all labeled $a$?

6. Write an expression for the area of each small triangle using $a$ and the variables $h_1$, $h_2$, and $h_3$.

7. Add the three areas and simplify your expression by taking out any common factors.

8. How is the sum in Question 7 related to the total area of the equilateral triangle? Write an equation to show this relationship using $A$ for the area of the equilateral triangle.

9. Use your equation from Question 8 to explain why the sum of the distances to all three sides of a given equilateral triangle is always constant.

10. Drag $P$ to a vertex point. How is the sum of the distances related to the altitude of the original triangle in this case?

11. Your explanations in Questions 5, 8, and 9 would not work if the triangle were not equilateral. Why not?

## Present Your Explanation

Summarize your explanation of your original conjecture. You can use Questions 5–11 to help you. You may write your explanation as an argument in paragraph form or as a two-column proof. Use the back of this page, another sheet of paper, a Sketchpad sketch, or some other medium.

© 2003 Key Curriculum Press

## Further Exploration

**1.** Construct any triangle *ABC* and an arbitrary point *P* inside it. Where should you locate *P* to minimize the sum of the distances to all three sides of the triangle?

**2. a.** Construct any rhombus and an arbitrary point *P* inside it. Where should you locate *P* to minimize the sum of the distances to all four sides of the rhombus?

**b.** Explain your observation in Question 2a and generalize to polygons with a similar property.

**3. a.** Construct any parallelogram and an arbitrary point *P* inside it. Where should you locate *P* to minimize the sum of the distances to all four sides of the parallelogram?

**b.** Explain your observation in Question 3a and generalize to polygons with a similar property.

**4.** Construct a (non-regular) pentagon with all angles equal and an arbitrary point *P* inside it. What do you notice about the distances to the sides of the pentagon? Can you generalize further?

**Historical Note:**
The result that the sum of the distances from a point to the sides of an equilateral triangle is constant is known as Viviani's theorem. Viviani was a student of the seventeenth-century Italian mathematician and scientist Evangelista Torricelli (also see the activity Airport Problem).

**5.** The dynamic Sketchpad scale drawing of the equilateral triangle is an example of a *mathematical model* that can be used to represent and analyze real-world situations. However, real-world situations are extremely complex and usually have to be simplified before mathematics can be meaningfully applied to them. What are some of the assumptions that could have been made above to simplify the original problem for an equilateral triangle?

In a developing country such as South Africa, there are many remote rural areas where people do not have access to safe, clean water and are dependent on nearby rivers and streams for their water supply. Apart from being unreliable due to frequent droughts, these rivers and streams are often muddy and unfit for human consumption. Suppose the government wants to build a water reservoir and purification plant for four villages in such a remote rural area. Where should the government place the water reservoir so that it is the same distance from all four villages?

## INVESTIGATE

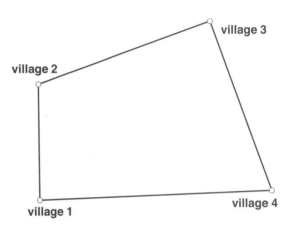

**1.** Before you work in Sketchpad, draw a point in the drawing that shows your best guess for the location of the reservoir. Label the point *P*.

☞ Open the sketch **Water Supply I.gsp,** which shows the map in the drawing.

☞ Construct a point *P* anywhere to represent the water reservoir.

To measure the distance between two points, select both points and choose **Distance** from the Measure menu.

☞ Measure the distances from the point *P* to each of the four vertices.

☞ Drag point *P* and observe the four distance measurements. Try to locate point *P* so that it is the same distance from all four vertices.

**2.** Were you able to locate point *P* so that the four distances were equal? If so, how does the location you found in the Sketchpad sketch compare with your guess in Question 1? If not, what did you discover in trying?

## A Simpler Problem

How can you locate point *P* precisely without using trial and error and dragging? In problem solving, it is often useful to look at a *simpler case* of a problem. In the original problem, we wanted to find a point that is *equidistant* (at equal distances) from four vertices. A simpler case would be to look for a point (or points) equidistant from just two vertices.

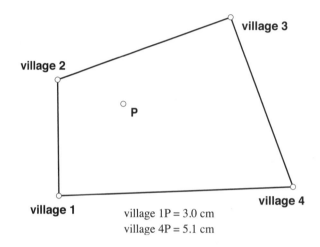

village 1P = 3.0 cm
village 4P = 5.1 cm

Continue in the same sketch, but focus on only two adjacent vertices for now.

It may help to drag the two extra measurements off to the side or hide them, leaving behind only the measurements related to the two vertices you have chosen to focus on.

☞ If necessary, drag point *P* so that it is equidistant from two adjacent vertices.

☞ Select point *P* and choose **Trace Point** from the Display menu.

☞ Drag point *P* slowly for a few centimeters, keeping it as close to equidistant as possible from the two adjacent vertices.

**3.** Describe as many properties as you can that relate the traced path to the segment connecting the two vertices.

CHALLENGE    Use your observations from Question 3 to revisit the original problem with all four villages. Come up with an alternative way to search for a point equidistant from all four vertices. Describe your construction method here. If you get stuck, continue reading.

On the previous page, you should have found that there are an infinite number of points that lie equidistant from two vertices and that they all lie on a straight line. Furthermore, from symmetry you may notice that folding around this line of equidistant points maps one village onto the other; therefore, this line *bisects* the line segment connecting the villages and is perpendicular to it. This line of equidistant points is called the *perpendicular bisector* of a line segment.

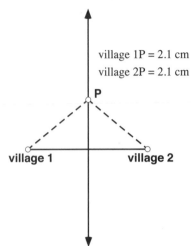

village 1P = 2.1 cm
village 2P = 2.1 cm

P

village 1          village 2

To construct a perpendicular bisector in Sketchpad, first select the segment and choose **Midpoint** from the Construct menu. Then select the midpoint and the segment and choose **Perpendicular Line** from the Construct menu.

☞ If your villages have moved during your construction, use the action button to snap them to their correct locations.

☞ Construct all four perpendicular bisectors of the sides of the quadrilateral.

**4.** What do you notice about the four perpendicular bisectors of this quadrilateral?

## A More General Problem

**5.** Do you think you can always find a point equidistant from all four vertices of a quadrilateral, no matter what the shape or size of the quadrilateral? Explain.

**6.** Drag any vertex of the quadrilateral. What do you notice about the perpendicular bisectors?

**7.** Do you still agree with your answer to Question 5? Explain.

☞ Use the button in your sketch to return the villages to their correct locations.

☞ Drag point *P* to the point that is equidistant from all four vertices.

☞ Construct a circle with *P* as its center and a village on the circumference.

**8.** Record what you observe about the other vertices of the quadrilateral and explain why this must be true.

## Further Exploration

**1.** In a new sketch, construct a quadrilateral and a central point so that the point is always equidistant from all four vertices. Make the quadrilateral as general as possible. Make sure the central point is always equidistant from the vertices, no matter which points you drag. Explain your construction method.

**2.** The dynamic Sketchpad scale drawing of the four villages is an example of a mathematical model that can be used to represent and analyze real-world situations. However, real-world situations are extremely complex and usually have to be simplified before mathematics can be meaningfully applied to them. What are some of the assumptions that could have been made above to simplify the original problem?

**3.** Suppose there is no equidistant point for four villages (that is, the perpendicular bisectors are not concurrent). Investigate what might be the "best" position to now place the water reservoir. Can you mathematically explain why you think that would be the "best" position?

**4.** Suppose you are sailing on a boat around an island as indicated here. At what locations on the route should you be to be able to determine which of the buildings *A*, *B*, or *C* is the tallest and which is the shortest? Explain your reasoning. (All buildings stand on the same level and are visible anywhere along the indicated route.)

The government needs to build a water reservoir for the three villages shown below. Where should the water reservoir be placed so that it is equidistant from all three villages?

## INVESTIGATE

1. Before you work in Sketchpad, draw a point in the drawing that shows your best guess for the location of the reservoir. Label the point *P*.

👉 Open the sketch **Water Supply II.gsp,** which shows the map in the drawing.

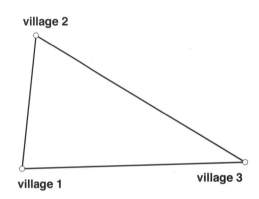

👉 Construct the perpendicular bisectors of two sides of the triangle to locate the reservoir correctly in your sketch.

> To construct a perpendicular bisector in Sketchpad, first select the segment and choose **Midpoint** from the Construct menu. Then select the midpoint and the segment and choose **Perpendicular Line** from the Construct menu.

2. How does your reservoir location compare to the location in your initial guess?

## A More General Problem

3. Do you think you can always find a point equidistant from all three vertices, no matter what the shape or size of the triangle? Explain.

4. Drag any vertex of the triangle. What do you notice about the perpendicular bisectors? Do you still agree with your answer in Question 3? Explain.

## EXPLAINING

In the activity Water Supply I: Four Towns, you found that the perpendicular bisectors of a quadrilateral do not always meet in one point; in other words, the perpendicular bisectors of the sides of a quadrilateral are not always concurrent. However, in that activity you should have discovered the rather surprising result that the perpendicular bisectors of any triangle are always concurrent at a point equidistant from all three vertices. This point of concurrency is called the *circumcenter* of the triangle since it is the center of the circle (the *circumcircle*) that passes through all three vertices.

If you came up with your own explanation as to why the perpendicular bisectors of any triangle are concurrent, compare it with the one that follows. If not, work through this investigation:

Let *P* be the point of intersection of two of your perpendicular bisectors. We will show logically that this point *P* must also lie on the perpendicular bisector of the third side; that is, all three perpendicular bisectors of a triangle always meet in the same point.

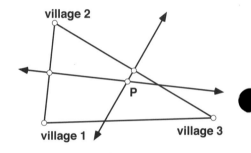

**5.** Pick one of the two perpendicular bisectors. What can you say about all the points on this bisector?

**6.** What can you say about all the points on the other perpendicular bisector?

**7.** What can you therefore say about *P*, the point of intersection of both perpendicular bisectors?

**8.** What can you therefore conclude about *P* and the perpendicular bisector of the third side?

## Present Your Explanation

Summarize your explanation using your answers to Questions 5–8. Your summary may be in paper form or electronic form and may include a presentation sketch in Sketchpad. You may want to discuss the summary with your partner or group.

## Further Exploration

1. When is the circumcenter of a triangle inside, outside, or on the perimeter of a triangle?

2. Construct a general quadrilateral *ABCD* and any three of its perpendicular bisectors. Construct the intersection of two of these perpendicular bisectors and use it as a center to construct a circle that always passes through three of the vertices.

   a. Drag the vertices of the quadrilateral until all three perpendicular bisectors are concurrent. What do you notice?

   b. Drag the quadrilateral to a different shape until all three perpendicular bisectors are again concurrent. Also, construct the fourth perpendicular bisector. What do you notice?

   c. In the space below, write a conjecture about your observations. Can you explain why it is true? Can you generalize further to pentagons, hexagons, and so on? Discuss with your partner or group.

You'll begin this investigation by making a conjecture about the sum of the measures of the angles in a triangle. Then you'll make sketches to help explain why your conjecture is true.

## CONJECTURE

☞ Open the sketch **Triangle Sum.gsp.**

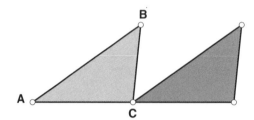

☞ Translate the triangle by vector *AC* by pressing the button. Drag a vertex and observe your sketch.

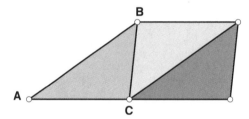

☞ Rotate △*ABC* by 180° about the midpoint of $\overline{BC}$ by pressing the button.

**1.** Drag a vertex of your original triangle. What can you say about the three angles that now meet at point *C* of the original triangle?

**2.** Use your construction to make a conjecture about the sum of the angles of a triangle. (This is often called the Triangle Sum Conjecture.)

# EXPLAINING

You are now probably quite convinced, after the preceding investigation, that the sum of the angles of a triangle is always equal to the measure of a straight line (or 180°). Further exploration on the same sketch would probably succeed in convincing you more fully, but it really provides no explanation; it merely keeps on confirming the statement's truth. Instead, we will now try to explain your conjecture as a consequence of other, more basic geometric ideas.

It is customary to provide reasons for each step in our explanation.

Here are some hints for planning a possible explanation based on the last sketch you constructed:

☞ Use the appropriate buttons to hide the two new triangles so that only triangle *ABC* is showing.

☞ Press the button to show ray *AC* and point *D*.

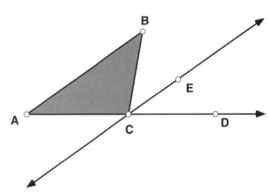

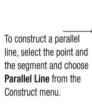
To construct a parallel line, select the point and the segment and choose **Parallel Line** from the Construct menu.

☞ Construct a line parallel to $\overline{AB}$ through point *C*.

☞ Construct point *E*, as shown.

☞ Drag point *A* to observe the behavior of this construction.

**3.** What is the relationship between ∠*BAC* and ∠*ECD*? Why?

**4.** What is the relationship between ∠*ABC* and ∠*BCE*? Why?

**5.** What can you say about the sum of the measures of ∠*ACB*, ∠*BCE*, and ∠*ECD*? Why?

6. What can you conclude from Questions 3–5 regarding the sum of the measures of ∠ACB, ∠ABC, and ∠BAC?

7. Which properties of straight and parallel lines did you use here to explain why the sum of the measures of the angles of a triangle is 180°?

## Present Your Explanation

Summarize your explanation of the Triangle Sum Conjecture. You may use Questions 3–7 to help you. You might write your explanation as an argument in paragraph form or as a two-column proof. Use the back of this page, another sheet of paper, a Sketchpad sketch, or some other medium.

## Further Exploration

1. The construction at right provides you with another method of explaining the Triangle Sum Conjecture.

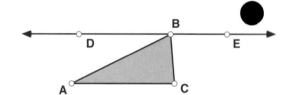

Start with △ABC. Construct a line parallel to $\overline{AC}$ through point B. Construct points D and E on the new parallel line as shown.

a. Use your new sketch and the properties of parallel lines to explain the Triangle Sum Conjecture.

b. How is this explanation different from the one in Questions 3–7?

In this activity, you will investigate a quadrilateral tessellation and discover and explain an interesting property of quadrilaterals.

## CONJECTURE

☞ Open the sketch **Quad Sum.gsp.** Press the buttons to rotate each quadrilateral.

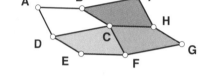

☞ Reset your sketch. Change the shape of quadrilateral *ABCD* and rotate each quadrilateral again.

**1.** Explain how the four quadrilaterals are related.

**2.** Look at the four angles around vertex *C*. State whether there are any overlaps or gaps between the angles. Also describe the sum of their measures.

**3.** Drag any vertex of quadrilateral *ABCD* to change the quadrilateral. Are your observations from Question 2 still true?

**4.** Carefully compare the angles around vertex *C* with the interior angles of quadrilateral *ABCD*. Measure some angles, if necessary.

**a.** What can you say about ∠*ADC* and ∠*FCD*? Why?

**b.** What can you say about ∠*BAD* and ∠*HCF*? Why?

To measure an angle, select three points, using the vertex as the middle selection. Then choose **Angle** from the Measure menu.

**c.** What can you say about ∠*CBA* and ∠*BCH*? Why?

**5.** What can you therefore say about the sum of the interior angles of *ABCD*?

**6.** Drag a vertex until *ABCD* is concave.
Does your conjecture still appear to be true?

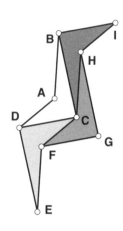

CHALLENGE     Try to logically explain your conjecture from Question 5
by writing a carefully structured argument based on the
preceding exploration. If you get stuck or want some
hints, continue reading.

● **EXPLAINING**

There are several different ways to construct logical explanations as to why the sum of the measures of the interior angles of any convex or concave quadrilateral is 360°. Questions 7 and 8 show two possible ways.

**7.** Reset your sketch. Construct a diagonal that divides the quadrilateral into two triangles. Drag your quadrilateral to make sure this construction holds for both convex and concave cases. Now use what you know about the sum of the measures of the angles of a triangle to explain why the sum of the measures of the interior angles of any quadrilateral is 360°.

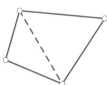

**8.** Recall that the sum of the measures of the exterior angles of a polygon is always 360° (as long as none of the sides of the polygon cross). Use this exterior angle sum result to determine the interior angle sum of a quadrilateral.

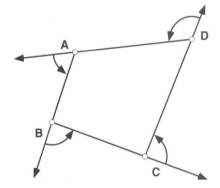

**Present Your Explanation**

Write out one or both of your logical explanations clearly for presentation to the class or to your group. Your summary may be in paper form or electronic form and may include a presentation sketch in Sketchpad. You may want to discuss the summary with your partner or group.

**Further Exploration**

Investigate the interior angle sums for convex or concave pentagons, hexagons, and so on. Can you derive a general formula for the interior angle sum of any given convex or concave polygon?

You may have already made a conjecture about the sum of the angles in a convex or concave quadrilateral. You may have also explained why the conjecture is true. Does that conjecture apply to quadrilaterals that cross themselves? In this activity, you'll investigate that question.

## CONJECTURE

✎ Open the sketch **Crossed Quad Sum.gsp.** This sketch shows a convex quadrilateral and its angle measures.

✎ Drag any vertex and observe the angle measures and sum. For now, keep the quadrilateral convex.

1. Write down what you observe about the sum of the measures of the interior angles in a convex quadrilateral.

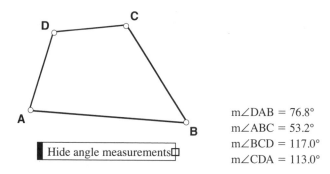

m∠DAB = 76.8°
m∠ABC = 53.2°
m∠BCD = 117.0°
m∠CDA = 113.0°

✎ Drag a vertex so that the quadrilateral is concave and observe the angle measures and sum as you drag.

2. What do you observe about the angle sum in concave quadrilaterals? Is that what you expected to happen? Why or why not?

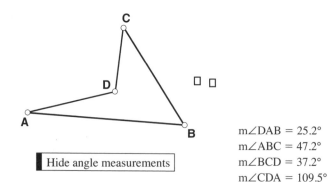

m∠DAB = 25.2°
m∠ABC = 47.2°
m∠BCD = 37.2°
m∠CDA = 109.5°

3. In your sketch, draw the diagonal of the concave quadrilateral. If you've explained why the quadrilateral angle sum conjecture is true for convex quadrilaterals, think about that explanation. In what way or ways does your figure now contradict the measures and angle sum Sketchpad is displaying?

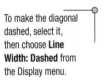

To make the diagonal dashed, select it, then choose **Line Width: Dashed** from the Display menu.

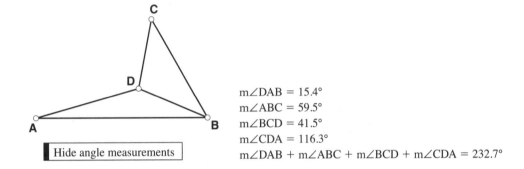

m∠DAB = 15.4°
m∠ABC = 59.5°
m∠BCD = 41.5°
m∠CDA = 116.3°
m∠DAB + m∠ABC + m∠BCD + m∠CDA = 232.7°

Confused? You should be! If you understand the explanation as to why the sum of the measures of the interior angles of a quadrilateral is 360°, you should see that it should apply to concave as well as convex quadrilaterals. Yet Sketchpad does not report the sum as 360° in concave quadrilaterals. What's going on? Is the explanation wrong? Is Sketchpad broken? In the next questions and steps, you'll discover what's going on and how to remedy the problem.

4. Look at the figure in Question 3. Three of the four interior angle measures are correct, but one of the measures is not of an interior angle. This is because Sketchpad always shows angle measures less than 180°. Identify the angle in the figure whose measure is greater than 180°, calculate its measure, and write it below. Does using this measure give you 360° for the sum of the interior angles in the figure?

An angle with measure greater than 180°, like the angle you identified in Question 4, is called a *reflex angle*. As you've discovered, Sketchpad doesn't measure reflex angles. However, Sketchpad does measure arc angles, and arc angle measures can be greater than 180°. Arcs will solve our problem of measuring reflex angles.

👉 Press the *Show arc angles* button.

👉 Drag a vertex of the quadrilateral and observe the arc angle measures and their sum.

**5.** Which measures—the simple angle measures or the arc angle measures—do you think are more useful for investigating the interior angles of a general (convex or concave) quadrilateral? Why?

👉 Select the diagonal and delete it.

**6.** Before dragging any farther, what do you think will happen to the sum of the measures of the interior angles if two sides of quadrilateral *ABCD* are crossed?

👉 Now drag a vertex of your quadrilateral until it becomes a crossed quadrilateral. Observe what happens to the arcs and to the measures as you drag a vertex around.

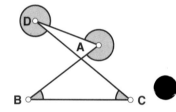

**7.** You should observe that two of the arcs in any crossed quadrilateral are always reflex angles. Does it make sense to call these reflex angles "interior" angles? Why or why not?

"Yes" and "no" are both acceptable answers to Question 7. You may object to calling the reflex angles "interior" angles because they seem to fall outside the polygon. On the other hand, when a polygon crosses itself, it's no longer obvious what the outside or the inside is. It's possible to define the interior angles of a crossed quadrilateral in a way that's consistent with non-crossed quadrilaterals.

Imagine you're walking around the first quadrilateral shown on the next page, alphabetically, from *A* to *B* to *C* and so on. The interior of the quadrilateral is always to your left. Now imagine you're walking around the second quadrilateral, from *A* to *B* to *C* and so on. This quadrilateral has a different orientation, but it's still clear where the interior is: It's to your right. So as you walk around, the interior angles of a quadrilateral can all be either on the right or on the left.

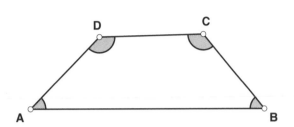

The interior is to your left as you walk from *A* to *B* to *C* and so on.

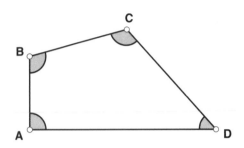

The interior is to your right as you walk from *A* to *B* to *C* and so on.

In a crossed quadrilateral, like either of those shown below, it's arbitrary whether the interior is to your right or your left as you walk around. So for the purpose of defining the interior angles, stay with what you know about non-crossed quadrilaterals: The angles are all on the right as you walk around, or they're all on the left. In a crossed quadrilateral, you can call either set the "interior" angles.

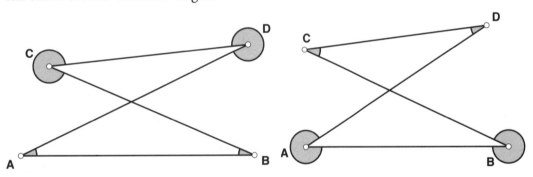

The set of interior angles is to your left as you walk from *A* to *B* to *C* and so on.

The set of interior angles is to your right as you walk from *A* to *B* to *C* and so on.

☞ Drag a vertex to observe various different crossed quadrilaterals.

**8.** According to the definition of interior angles given above, what is the sum of the measures of the interior angles of a crossed quadrilateral?

**9.** You can keep dragging until you cross another pair of sides. (In a sense, you are turning the quadrilateral inside out.) Describe your results. Which correctly reports the interior angle sum: the simple angle measures, the arc angle measures, or neither? Explain.

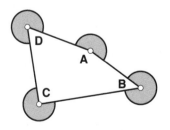

CHALLENGE  Explain your observations in Question 8. Can you derive a general formula for the interior angle sum of any given convex, concave, or crossed polygon?

# EXPLAINING

Work through the steps below to explain logically why the measures of the interior angles of a crossed quadrilateral add up to 720°.

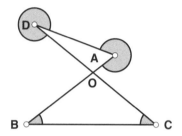

**10.** Express the measures of reflex angles *ADC* and *BAD* respectively in terms of the measures of acute angles *ADC* and *BAD*.

**11.** Express the measure of angle *BOD* in terms of the measures of acute angles *ADC* and *BAD*. Explain your expression.

**12.** Express the measure of angle *BOD* in terms of the measures of angles *BCD* and *ABC*. Explain your expression.

**13.** From Questions 11 and 12, what can you now conclude about the relationship between the sum of the measures of acute angles *ADC* and *BAD*, and about the sum of the measures of angles *BCD* and *ABC*?

**14.** From Question 13, what can you now conclude about the sum of the measures of reflex angle *ADC*, reflex angle *BAD*, angle *BCD*, and angle *ABC*?

## Present Your Explanation

Write out your explanation for presentation to the class or to your group. Your summary may be in paper form or electronic form and may include a presentation sketch in Sketchpad. You may want to discuss the summary with your partner or your group.

In this activity, you will construct an isosceles trapezoid. Then you will discover some of the properties of this special quadrilateral and explain why an isosceles quadrilateral has these properties.

## CONJECTURE

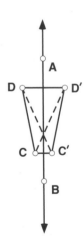

👉 In a new sketch, construct a vertical line *AB*.

👉 Construct any two points *C* and *D* not on the line.

To reflect points across a line, double-click on the line to mark it as a mirror. Then select both points and choose **Reflect** from the Transform menu.

👉 Reflect *C* and *D* across the line.

👉 Connect points *C*, *D*, *C′*, and *D′* to form a quadrilateral.

👉 Measure the lengths of all four sides of your isosceles trapezoid.

**1.** Drag any point in your sketch. What do you observe about the sides of an isosceles trapezoid?

To measure an angle, select three points on the angle, making sure your middle selection is the angle's vertex. Then choose **Angle** from the Measure menu.

👉 Measure all four angles of your isosceles trapezoid.

**2.** What do you observe about the angles of an isosceles trapezoid?

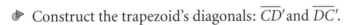

👉 Construct the trapezoid's diagonals: $\overline{CD'}$ and $\overline{DC'}$.

👉 Select both diagonals, and in the Display menu, change **Line Width** to **Dashed.**

👉 Measure the lengths of the diagonals.

**3.** Drag any point in your sketch. What do you observe about the diagonals of an isosceles trapezoid?

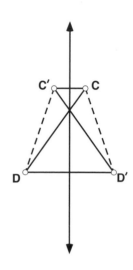

4. A *crossed quadrilateral* has two intersecting sides. As you may have already noticed, you can turn your isosceles quadrilateral into a crossed quadrilateral. Which, if any, of your observations from Questions 1–3 still hold for crossed isosceles trapezoids?

5. What do you notice about the Sketchpad measures of a crossed isosceles trapezoid that is not always true for a convex isosceles trapezoid?

# EXPLAINING

Next, you will explain *why* your conjectures are true.

6. First, explain your conjectures in Questions 1–4 above. (*Hint:* Think about the way you constructed the isosceles trapezoid and its axis of symmetry.)

7. Now explain your conjecture from Question 5. (*Hint:* Look at the four triangles created by the four sides of the quadrilateral. Hide the diagonals if they get in your way.)

## Further Exploration

1. Drag your isosceles trapezoid so that all four of its angles are equal, but it is still convex. Is it still an isosceles trapezoid? Explain.

2. This time make all four sides equal. Is your quadrilateral still an isosceles trapezoid? Explain.

3. Can you drag your isosceles trapezoid into all the possible shapes of a parallelogram? How about a kite? Explain.

4. Can you construct a circle that always passes through all four vertices of your isosceles trapezoid? (*Hint:* Construct the perpendicular bisectors of all four sides of your isosceles trapezoid.) Explain your construction in terms of symmetry.

# Cyclic Quadrilateral

In this activity, you will investigate some properties of a quadrilateral inscribed in a circle—in other words, a quadrilateral whose vertices lie on a circle. Such a quadrilateral is called a *cyclic quadrilateral.*

## CONJECTURE

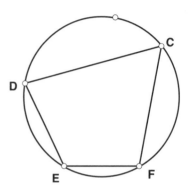

☞ Open the sketch **Cyclic Quad.gsp.**

☞ Use Sketchpad's calculator to sum each pair of opposite angles.

**1.** Drag a vertex. What can you say about the two pairs of opposite angles of a cyclic quadrilateral? (You may have dragged the vertex enough to cross the sides of the quadrilateral. Do not worry about these "crossed quadrilaterals" for now.)

**2.** Press the *Show perpendicular lines* button. What do you notice about the perpendicular bisectors of a cyclic quadrilateral?

### Further Exploration

Can you drag your cyclic quadrilateral into the general shapes of some of the special quadrilaterals that you've already seen? For example, try making a kite, an isosceles trapezoid, a parallelogram, a rhombus, a rectangle, and a square.

# EXPLAINING

In the preceding section, you discovered the following:

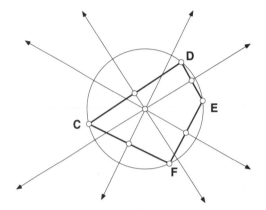

$m\angle CDE + m\angle EFC = 180.0°$
$m\angle DEF + m\angle FCD = 180.0°$

- Opposite angles of a cyclic quadrilateral are supplementary (as long as the quadrilateral is not crossed).

- The perpendicular bisectors of the sides of a cyclic quadrilateral always remain concurrent at the center of the circle. This center is called the *circumcenter* of the cyclic quadrilateral.

3. You will explain the second conjecture first. Write an explanation below for the concurrency of the perpendicular bisectors of a cyclic quadrilateral. (*Hint:* First explain why *each* perpendicular bisector goes through the center of the circle. Construct radii to help.)

4. Recall that an inscribed angle has half the measure of its intercepted arc (see the diagram). Use this result to explain why in a cyclic quadrilateral the opposite angles are supplementary. (*Hint:* In your original sketch, construct chord *DF*.)

$m\angle XYZ = 35°$

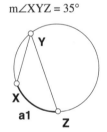

m arc angle a1 = 70°

## Further Exploration

In the cyclic hexagon shown on the right, the angles $C$, $E$, and $G$ are called *alternate* angles. Similarly, angles $D$, $F$, and $H$ are alternate angles.

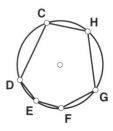

**1.** Construct a cyclic hexagon, measure its angles, and calculate the sum of both sets of alternate angles. What do you notice?

**2.** In your own words, formulate a conjecture based on your observation in Question 1.

**3.** Can you logically explain your conjecture in Question 2? (*Hint:* Draw a diagonal so that the cyclic hexagon is divided into two cyclic quadrilaterals.)

**4.** Which are the alternate angles in a cyclic quadrilateral *ABCD*? Reformulate your earlier result for cyclic quadrilaterals in terms of alternate angles.

**5.** Can you generalize your conjecture for a cyclic hexagon further, to cyclic octagons, cyclic decagons, and so on? In other words, generalize to cyclic $2n$-gons where $n > 1$.

# The Center of Gravity of a Triangle

The balancing point of a two- or three-dimensional object is called its *center of gravity*. In architecture and engineering, accurately locating balancing points is extremely important for designing stable structures that do not collapse. You can locate the center of gravity of an object through experimentation. For example, when you balance a cardboard polygon on the tip of a pencil or an eraser, you have found the center of gravity of the polygon.

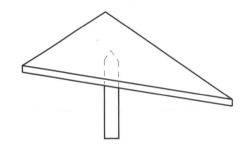

The pictures here show another way of locating the center of gravity of a cardboard polygon. The polygon is hanging on a string that is attached near its edge. The string is acting as a carpenter's plumb line, which provides the carpenter with a line perpendicular to the ground.

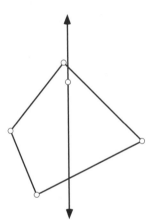

This quadrilateral is hanging by one point from a makeshift plumb line.

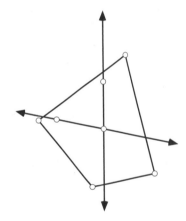

The same quadrilateral is hanging from a plumb line by a different point. The line of the previous plumb line is still showing.

The center of gravity is located where these two lines cross. Can you see why?

When you use experimentation to locate centers of gravity, the results are obviously subject to some experimental error.

In the following investigation, you will discover an accurate geometric way of locating the center of gravity of any triangle. The center of gravity of a triangle is also called a *centroid*. Imagine a triangle made up of thin horizontal beams, as shown here. Where is the center of gravity of each of these beams located? What can you conjecture about them?

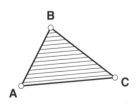

## CONJECTURE: LOCATING THE CENTROID

✥ Open the sketch **Triangle Median.gsp.**

1. Drag point *D*. How is $\overline{DE}$ related to $\overline{AC}$?

2. Where is the center of gravity of $\overline{DE}$ located?

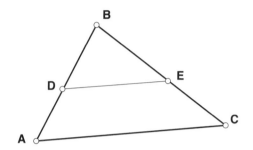

✥ Construct the center of gravity *F* of $\overline{DE}$.

3. Predict the path of *F* as *D* is dragged along $\overline{AB}$. Sketch your prediction in the triangle at right.

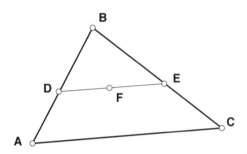

To trace point *F*, select *F* and choose **Trace Midpoint** from the Display menu. To turn off tracing, select *F* and again choose **Trace Midpoint** from the Display menu.

✥ Turn on tracing for point *F*. Now drag point *D* along $\overline{AB}$.

4. Describe the path of point *F*.

With point *F* still selected, also select point *D* and choose **Locus** from the Construct menu.

✥ Since the trace disappears when you click elsewhere, it is helpful to have a permanent *locus* of the path of *F*. Turn off tracing and construct this locus.

5. This path of point *F* is called a *median*. Briefly explain why the centroid of the whole triangle must lie somewhere on this median.

6. Write a definition (description) of a median.

7. Describe a shorter way to construct a median.

✥ Now use your method from Question 7 to construct the other two medians of the triangle.

8. Drag a vertex of your triangle. What can you say about the intersection of the three medians of a triangle?

## CONJECTURE: THE PROPERTIES OF THE CENTROID

In this investigation, you'll discover and prove some interesting properties of the centroid of a triangle.

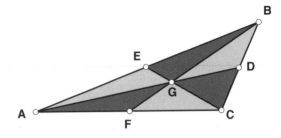

☞ Open the sketch **Centroid.gsp** and drag a vertex to experiment with the sketch.

**9.** The medians of $\triangle ABC$ are _____ , _____ , and _____ . The centroid is _____ .

☞ Show the distances along the medians. Also show the ratios of the distances.

**10.** Drag a vertex of your triangle. Write a conjecture about how the centroid $G$ divides each median in a triangle.

☞ Hide the distances and their ratios and show the areas of the smaller triangles.

**11.** Drag a vertex and observe any relationships among the six areas. Write a conjecture about the areas of the smaller triangles formed by the three medians.

Although you are no doubt already convinced about your observations above, can you explain, in terms of other well-known geometric results, why your observations are true?

Mathematicians find the explanatory value of a logical argument useful. They also perceive the finding or development of a suitable explanation as an intellectual challenge. To them, it is as appealing as the solution of a complicated puzzle or a brain teaser, and as rewarding as the production of an original piece of music, art, or poetry. It could also be compared to the physical challenge of completing an arduous marathon or other physical task because it is a test of the intellectual ingenuity and stamina of the mathematician.

CHALLENGE     Try to logically explain any of the conjectures you have made in this activity. After you have thought for a while and made some notes, use the hints that follow to develop an explanation of the three conjectures.

In the preceding investigations you should have made three separate conjectures:

The three medians of a triangle always intersect in one point, and this point of concurrency is the centroid.

The centroid divides each median into the ratio 2:1.

The six small triangles *AFG*, *CGF*, *GDC*, *BDG*, *GEB*, and *AGE* have equal areas.

## EXPLAINING

You will begin by explaining the first two conjectures. Think through the sketch again. Segments *AD* and *CE* are medians intersecting at point *G*. Imagine joining *B* with *G* and extending this segment to *F* on $\overline{AC}$. We need to prove that *F* must always be the midpoint of $\overline{AC}$ (in other words, that $\overline{BF}$ is also a median and therefore all three meet in the same point *G*).

To extend $\overline{BF}$ this way, try using a circle and the **Ray** tool, or translate by a marked vector using commands from the Transform menu.

▷ Figure out a way to extend $\overline{BF}$ to *H* so that $\overline{GH} = \overline{GB}$. Drag a vertex of the original triangle to check your construction.

▷ Construct $\overline{HA}$ and $\overline{HC}$.

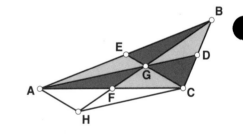

**12.** In △*ABH*, what can you say about $\overline{EG}$ in relation to $\overline{AH}$? Why?

**13.** In △*CBH*, what can you say about $\overline{DG}$ in relation to $\overline{CH}$? Why?

**14.** Using Questions 12 and 13, what kind of quadrilateral is *AHCG*? Drag points to test your conclusion.

**15.** From Question 14, what can you now conclude about the diagonals $\overline{AC}$ and $\overline{GH}$ of quadrilateral *AHCG*?

**16.** What can you conclude about *F*?

**17.** From Question 16, what can you now also say about $\overline{FG}$ in relation to $\overline{GB}$? Why?

Next, you'll explain why the six triangles have equal areas.

**18.** Consider the areas of the following pairs of adjacent triangles: *AFG* and *CFG* (shown in the picture), *CDG* and *BDG*, and *BEG* and *AEG*. Why are their areas equal?

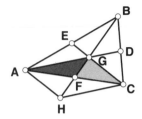

**19.** What can you say about the areas of triangles *AFB* and *CFB* (shown in the picture)? Why?

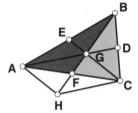

**20.** From Questions 18 and 19, what can you conclude about the areas of triangles *ABG* and *CBG*? Why?

**21.** What can you now conclude about the areas of triangles *CDG*, *BDG*, *BEG*, and *AEG*? Why?

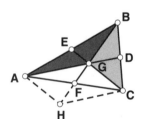

**22.** Now complete the logical explanation on your own.

## Present Your Explanation

Write full explanations of your three original conjectures. You can use Questions 12–22 to help you. You may write your explanation as an argument in paragraph form or as a two-column proof. Use the back of this page, another sheet of paper, a Sketchpad sketch, or some other medium.

## Further Exploration

1. **a.** Can you find a way using geometric constructions in Sketchpad to locate the center of gravity of any "cardboard" quadrilateral?

   **b.** Check your method in Question 1a with a concave quadrilateral. What do you notice about the center of gravity of a concave quadrilateral?

   **c.** Try to generalize your method in Question 1a to any polygon.

2. Track and field star Dick Fosbury changed the high jump event forever by popularizing the backward-flip approach that came to be known as the "Fosbury flop." Fosbury was a student at Oregon State University (1965–69) when he used the "flop" to set an Olympic record with a jump of 7 ft $4\frac{1}{2}$ in. in Mexico City on October 21, 1968. Much ridiculed at the time, Fosbury's "flop" method eventually replaced the former standard "straddle" and "scissors" methods to become the standard method of world-class high jumpers. Why has this method proved to be more effective? (*Hint:* It has something to do with the center of gravity.)

3. You can locate the centroid of a triangle using coordinate geometry.

   **a.** Measure the coordinates of the vertices of your triangle as well as its centroid. Calculate the average of the coordinates of the vertices. What do you notice? Check your observation by further dragging.

   **b.** Assume that the vertices of a triangle have coordinates $(x_1, y_1)$, $(x_2, y_2)$, and $(x_3, y_3)$. Show that the centroid is located at the "average" coordinates

$$\left( \frac{x_1 + x_2 + x_3}{3}, \frac{y_1 + y_2 + y_3}{3} \right)$$

   **c.** Use Sketchpad to find the "average" coordinates of the vertices of a quadrilateral and plot the point with those coordinates. Compare this point with the center of gravity of a "cardboard" quadrilateral as constructed in Question 1. What do you notice?

# 2

# Proof as

Discovery

In this investigation, you'll examine the quadrilateral formed by the midpoints of the sides of a kite. Before you begin this activity, make sure you know the properties of a kite and its diagonals.

## CONJECTURE

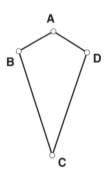

☞ Open the sketch **Kite.gsp.**

1. Drag any vertex of the quadrilateral. What features make you sure that this quadrilateral is a kite?

☞ Construct the midpoints of the sides of the kite.

☞ Connect the midpoints of the kite to construct quadrilateral *EFGH*. This is sometimes called the *midpoint quadrilateral.*

2. Drag any vertex of the kite. What kind of quadrilateral do you think *EFGH* is? Measure its angles if necessary.

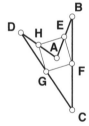

☞ Construct diagonals $\overline{AC}$ and $\overline{BD}$.

3. What happens if kite *ABCD* becomes concave? Does your observation about the midpoint quadrilateral still hold?

☞ Measure the lengths of both diagonals of *ABCD*.

4. Drag any of the points *A*, *B*, *C*, and *D*. Can *EFGH* ever be a square? If so, when?

In the preceding investigation, you should have found that

- The midpoint quadrilateral of a kite is a rectangle.

- The midpoint quadrilateral of a kite is a square only when the diagonals of the kite are congruent.

Although you are no doubt already convinced about these observations, can you *explain,* in terms of other geometric results, why your observations are true?

As before, further exploration on Sketchpad could probably succeed in convincing you even more fully, but knowing *why* something is true means understanding it much more deeply than just knowing from experimentation that it *is* true. This quest for deeper understanding is a powerful driving force not just in mathematics, but also in virtually all human intellectual pursuits.

For example, in physics, we want to understand why the planets revolve around the sun; in chemistry, why a certain chemical reacts with another, but not with some others; and in economics, why there is inflation.

## EXPLAINING

Before you explain the kite midpoint quadrilateral conjectures, you'll need to make a conjecture about triangles.

☞ In a new sketch, construct $\triangle ABC$.

☞ Construct midpoints $D$ and $E$ of sides $BC$ and $AB$.

☞ Construct $\overline{DE}$. We'll call this segment a *midsegment.*

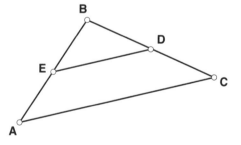

☞ Measure the lengths and the slopes of midsegment $DE$ and base $AC$.

☞ Measure the ratio $\frac{ED}{AC}$.

☞ Drag different vertices of the triangle and observe the measures and the ratio.

**5.** Write a conjecture about the relationship between a midsegment and the corresponding base of its triangle.

You can use the conjecture you just made to explain why the kite midpoint conjectures are true. An explanation as to why the triangle midsegment conjecture is true can wait until later, when you explore proof as systematization in Chapter 5. For now, you can just accept the truth of the triangle midsegment conjecture.

Here are some hints for planning possible explanations of the kite midpoint conjectures. Before reading the hints, you might want to take some time to try to construct your own explanations.

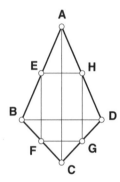

**6.** What is the relationship between $\overline{EF}$ and $\overline{AC}$ in $\triangle ACB$? Why?

**7.** What is the relationship between $\overline{HG}$ and $\overline{AC}$ in $\triangle ACD$? Why?

**8.** What can you therefore conclude about $\overline{EF}$ and $\overline{HG}$?

**9.** What is the relationship between $\overline{EH}$ and $\overline{BD}$ in $\triangle ABD$? Why?

**10.** What is the relationship between $\overline{FG}$ and $\overline{BD}$ in $\triangle CBD$? Why?

**11.** From Questions 9 and 10, what can you conclude about $\overline{EH}$ and $\overline{FG}$?

**12.** From Question 8 and/or Question 11, what can you conclude so far about the quadrilateral $EFGH$?

**13.** Given that the diagonals of a kite are always perpendicular (check if you like!), what can you now conclude about the relationships between adjacent sides of $EFGH$?

**14.** If $AC = BD$, what can you then say about the sides of $EFGH$?

# DISCOVERING

So far we've seen that new results in mathematics can be discovered by experimentation. Sometimes, however, you can make new discoveries simply by carefully reflecting on your logical explanations. A good explanation conveys insight into why something is true and can sometimes reveal that certain conditions are not necessary and that the result is therefore merely a special case of a more general one.

**15.** From Question 6 to your conclusion in Question 12, did you use any properties exclusive to kites?

**16.** What can you therefore deduce, from your conclusion in Question 12, about *any* quadrilateral? (Make a construction to check if you like.)

**17.** Apart from the property of perpendicular diagonals, did you use any other property exclusive to kites for your conclusion in Question 13? (For example, did you use the property that a kite has an axis of symmetry or two pairs of adjacent sides that are equal?)

**18.** Use Question 17 to describe the most generic quadrilateral that always has a rectangle as its midpoint quadrilateral.

**19.** Apart from the function of explanation, which is shown in the other activities, what new function of a logical argument is shown in Questions 15–18?

CHALLENGE   Use Sketchpad to construct the most generic quadrilateral whose midpoint quadrilateral is always a rectangle. When you succeed, describe your construction.

## Present Your Explanation

Summarize your explanation from Questions 6–14 and from your further discoveries in Questions 15–19. Your summary may be in paper form or electronic form and may include a presentation sketch in Sketchpad. You may want to discuss the summary with your partner or group.

In the preceding activities, you may have discovered geometric properties by first making a construction in Sketchpad and then producing a logical explanation as to why the property must hold true.

In mathematical research, experimentation does not always precede logical reasoning. As you will see in this activity, people also discover new geometric properties by logical reasoning first. Only afterward do they follow up with construction and measurement to make sure that false assumptions or conclusions have not been made.

## DISCOVERING

You have discovered previously that if you connect the midpoints of the sides of any quadrilateral, you get a _____ .

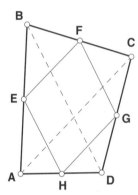

This result is also known as Varignon's theorem, named after Pierre Varignon, who first provided a logical explanation for it in 1731. Now, without using construction or measurement, work through the following questions using the diagram shown.

**1.** Write an equation relating the lengths *EF* and *HG* to the length *AC*.

**2.** Write an equation relating *EH* and *FG* to *BD*.

**3.** Explain how you found your equations in Questions 1 and 2.

**4.** Use Questions 1 and 2 to describe the relationship between the perimeter of the inscribed parallelogram *EFGH* and the diagonals of quadrilateral *ABCD*.

© 2003 Key Curriculum Press

## CHECK BY CONSTRUCTION

Make constructions with appropriate measurements in Sketchpad to confirm your conclusions from Question 4. Be sure to check the concave and crossed cases for quadrilateral *ABCD*. Summarize your results. Your summary may be in paper form or electronic form and may include a presentation sketch in Sketchpad. You may want to discuss the summary with your partner or group.

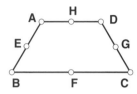

In this investigation, you'll learn about the kind of quadrilateral formed by the midpoints of the sides of an isosceles trapezoid.

## CONJECTURE

☞ Open the sketch **Iso Trap Mdpts.gsp.**

1. Drag any vertex of the quadrilateral. What features make you sure that this quadrilateral is an isosceles trapezoid?

☞ Press the button to show the midpoints of isosceles trapezoid *ABCD*.

☞ Press the button to connect the midpoints, forming *EFGH*. Such a quadrilateral is sometimes called a *midpoint quadrilateral*.

2. What kind of quadrilateral is the midpoint quadrilateral *EFGH*? Drag vertices and show measurements to test your conjecture.

☞ Press the button to show the diagonals of *ABCD*. This button also displays the measure of the angle at the intersection of the diagonals.

3. Drag any of the points *A*, *B*, *C*, and *D*. Can *EFGH* ever be a square? If so, when?

4. Drag a vertex of *ABCD* so that two of its sides are crossed. A quadrilateral like this is called a *crossed quadrilateral*. Do your observations from Questions 2 and 3 still hold if *ABCD* is crossed? Explain.

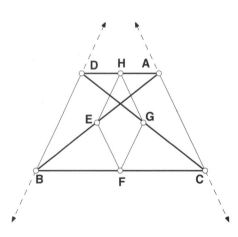

CHALLENGE    In the next part of this activity, you will explain *why* your conjectures from Questions 2 and 4 are true. Try to construct your own explanations before reading ahead to the hints that follow.

## EXPLAINING

You should have discovered two conjectures:

- The midpoint quadrilateral of an isosceles trapezoid is a rhombus.

- The midpoint quadrilateral of an isosceles trapezoid is a square only when the diagonals of the isosceles trapezoid are perpendicular to each other.

Although you are no doubt already convinced about these observations, can you *explain*, in terms of other geometric results, why your observations are true? Below are some questions for planning your explanations of your observations.

You will begin by explaining the first conjecture. Then in Question 12 you will explain the second conjecture.

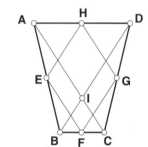

5. What is the relationship between $\overline{EF}$ and $\overline{AC}$ in $\triangle ACB$? Why?

6. What is the relationship between $\overline{HG}$ and $\overline{AC}$ in $\triangle ACD$? Why?

7. From Questions 5 and 6, what can you therefore conclude regarding $\overline{EF}$ and $\overline{HG}$?

8. What is the relationship between $\overline{EH}$ and $\overline{BD}$ in $\triangle ABD$? Why?

9. What is the relationship between $\overline{FG}$ and $\overline{BD}$ in $\triangle CBD$? Why?

10. From Questions 8 and 9, what can you conclude about $\overline{EH}$ and $\overline{FG}$?

11. Given that the lengths of the diagonals of an isosceles trapezoid are always equal (check if you like!), what can you now conclude about the relationships between the adjacent sides of quadrilateral *EFGH*?

12. If $\overline{AC} \perp \overline{BD}$, what can you then say about the angles of *EFGH*?

## DISCOVERING

13. Apart from the property of congruent diagonals, did you use any other property exclusive to isosceles trapezoids for your conclusion in Question 11? (For example, did you use the property that an isosceles trapezoid has one pair of parallel sides or one line of symmetry?)

14. Use Question 13 to describe the most generic quadrilateral that always has a rhombus as its midpoint quadrilateral.

15. So far we've seen that new results in mathematics can be discovered by experimentation, logical reasoning, or careful reflection on logical explanations. Which of these three different ways best describes your discovery in Question 13 or 14?

CHALLENGE Use Sketchpad to construct a generic quadrilateral whose midpoint quadrilateral is always a rhombus. The figure shown here gives a hint. When you succeed, describe your construction. You might also try constructing a generic quadrilateral whose midpoint quadrilateral is always a square.

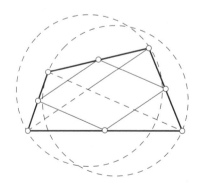

### Present Your Explanation

Summarize your explanation from Questions 5–12 and from your further discoveries in Questions 13 and 14. Your summary may be in paper form or electronic form and may include a presentation sketch in Sketchpad. You may want to discuss the summary with your partner or group.

© 2003 Key Curriculum Press

In earlier activities, you may have discovered geometric properties by making a construction in Sketchpad and then producing a logical explanation as to why the property must hold true.

In mathematical research, experimentation does not always precede logical reasoning. As you will see in this activity, people also discover new geometric properties by logical reasoning. Only afterward do they follow up with construction and measurement to make sure that false assumptions or conclusions have not been made.

## DISCOVERING

In this activity, you will logically deduce an interesting property of a quadrilateral with all its sides tangent to an inscribed circle—in other words, a quadrilateral circumscribed around a circle (a *circum quad rilateral*). Recall that the two tangents from a point outside a circle to the circle are equal in length.

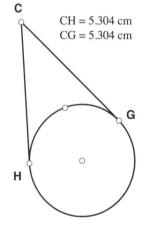

CH = 5.304 cm
CG = 5.304 cm

Now, without using construction or measurement, work through the following questions using the diagram that shows a quadrilateral with all four sides tangent to a circle (*circum quadrilateral*).

1. Consider vertex *A* of circum quadrilateral *ABCD*. What can you say about the distances *AP* and *AS*?

2. What can you say about the distances *BP* and *BQ,* the distances *CQ* and *CR,* and the distances *DR* and *DS*?

3. Label *AP* as *a*, *BP* as *b*, *CR* as *c*, and *DR* as *d*, and write an expression for *AB* + *CD*.

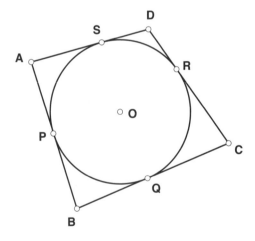

4. From your observations in Questions 1 and 2, write an expression in terms of *a*, *b*, *c*, and *d* for *BC* + *AD*.

5. Compare Question 3 with Question 4. What do you notice?

6. Formulate your conclusion in Question 5 in your own words and discuss it with your partner or group.

7. From Question 6, what type of quadrilateral would *ABCD* be if *AB* = *AD*?

## CHECK BY CONSTRUCTION

Open the sketch **Circum Quad.gsp** and make some measurements and calculations to confirm your conclusion from Question 6. You'll find that you can drag points *P*, *Q*, *R*, and *S*, but not points *A*, *B*, *C*, and *D*.

### Further Exploration

1. Construct the angle bisectors of all the angles of the circum quadrilateral. What do you notice? Can you explain your observation?

2. Which quadrilaterals (for example, parallelograms, rectangles, squares, kites, rhombuses, or squares) are special cases of a circum quadrilateral? Investigate by trying to drag your circum quadrilateral into the shapes of these special cases.

3. Is it possible to obtain a *concave* circum quadrilateral? If so, does your conjecture in Question 6 above still hold?

# 3

## Proof as

## Verification

In this activity, you will compare the area of an entire quadrilateral to that of a smaller quadrilateral constructed within it.

## CONJECTURE

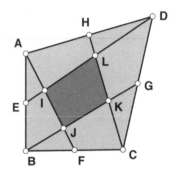

☞ Open the sketch **Areas.gsp.**

☞ Find the ratio of the area of quadrilateral *ABCD* to the area of quadrilateral *IJKL*.

> To find the ratio between two measurements, choose **Calculate** from the Measure menu and then click on a measurement to enter it into the Calculator.

**1.** What do you notice about this ratio?

**2.** Drag any vertex of quadrilateral *ABCD* to a new position. Does your observation still hold?

**3.** Summarize your observations above by writing a conjecture.

**4.** How certain are you that your conjecture is always true? Record your level of certainty on the number line and explain your choice.

```
    0%        25%        50%        75%       100%
```

**CHALLENGE**  If you believe your conjecture in Question 3 is always true, provide some examples to support your view and try to convince your partner or members of your group. Even better, support your conjecture with a logical explanation or a convincing proof. If you suspect your conjecture is not always true, try to supply counterexamples.

Repeat the previous investigation for a parallelogram.

👉 Open the sketch **Areas 2.gsp.**

👉 Again, find the ratio of the areas of the two quadrilaterals.

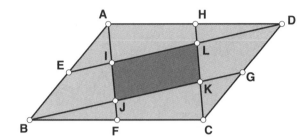

**5.** What do you now notice about this ratio?

> To find the ratio between two measurements, choose **Calculate** from the Measure menu and then click on a measurement to enter it into the calculator.

**6.** Drag any of the vertices of parallelogram *ABCD* to a new position. Does your observation/conjecture still hold?

**7.** Formulate a conjecture based on your observations.

**8.** How certain are you that your conjecture is always true? Record your level of certainty on the number line and explain your choice.

| 0% | 25% | 50% | 75% | 100% |

**CHALLENGE**   If you believe your conjecture is always true, provide some examples to support your view and try to convince your partner or members of your group. Even better, support your conjecture with a logical explanation or a convincing proof. If you suspect your conjecture or your partner's conjecture is not always true, try to supply counterexamples.

## EXPLAINING

Press the button *Half turn triangles.* What do you observe? Use your observation to explain why your conjecture is true for a parallelogram.

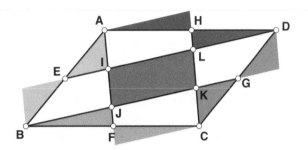

In this activity, you will compare the area of a quadrilateral to the area of another quadrilateral constructed inside it.

# CONJECTURE

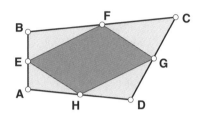

☞ Open the sketch **Varignon Area.gsp** and drag vertices to investigate the shapes in this sketch.

1. Points *E, F, G,* and *H* are midpoints of the sides of quadrilateral *ABCD*. Describe polygon *EFGH*.

☞ Press the appropriate button to show the areas of the two polygons you described. Drag a vertex and observe the areas.

2. Describe how the areas are related. You might want to find their ratio.

To find the ratio between two measurements, choose **Calculate** from the Measure menu and then click on a measurement to enter it into the calculator.

3. Drag any of the points *A, B, C,* and *D* and observe the two area measurements. Does the ratio between them change?

4. Drag a vertex of *ABCD* until it is concave. Does this change the ratio of the areas?

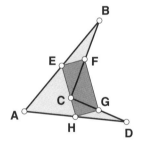

5. Write your discoveries so far as one or more conjectures. Use complete sentences.

6. You probably can think of times when something that always appeared to be true turned out to be false sometimes. (The previous activity, Areas, was a geometric example of this kind of occurrence.) How certain are you that your conjecture is always true? Record your level of certainty on the number line and explain your choice.

0%            25%            50%            75%            100%

CHALLENGE      If you believe your conjecture is always true, provide some examples to support your view and try to convince your partner or members of your group. Even better, support your conjecture with a logical explanation or a convincing proof. If you suspect your conjecture is not always true, try to supply counterexamples.

## PROVING

In the picture, you probably observed that quadrilateral *EFGH* is a parallelogram. You also probably made a conjecture that goes something like this:

> The area of the parallelogram formed by connecting the midpoints of the sides of a quadrilateral is half the area of the quadrilateral.

This first conjecture about quadrilateral *EFGH* matches a theorem of geometry that is sometimes called Varignon's theorem. Pierre Varignon was a priest and mathematician born in 1654 in Caen, France. He is known for his work with calculus and mechanics, including discoveries that relate fluid flow and water clocks.

The next three steps will help you verify that quadrilateral *EFGH* is a parallelogram. If you have verified this before, skip to Question 10.

**7.** Construct diagonal *AC*. How are $\overline{EF}$ and $\overline{HG}$ related to $\overline{AC}$? Why?

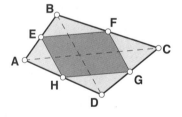

**8.** Construct diagonal *BD*. How are $\overline{EH}$ and $\overline{FG}$ related to $\overline{BD}$? Why?

**9.** Use Questions 7 and 8 to explain why *EFGH* must be a parallelogram.

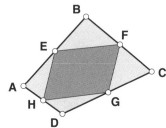

Work through the steps that follow for one possible explanation as to why parallelogram *EFGH* has half the area of quadrilateral *ABCD*. (If you have constructed diagonals in *ABCD*, it will help to delete or hide them.)

**10.** Assume for now that *ABCD* is convex. One way to explain why *ABCD* has twice the area of *EFGH* is to look at the regions that are inside *ABCD* but not inside *EFGH*. Describe these regions.

**11.** According to your conjecture, how should the total area of the regions you described in Question 10 compare with the area of *EFGH*?

▶ Press the button to translate the midpoint quadrilateral *EFGH* along vector *EF*.

**12.** Drag any point. How does the area of the translated quadrilateral compare to the area of *EFGH*?

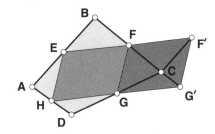

▶ Construct $\overline{F'C}$ and $\overline{G'C}$.

**13.** How is △*EBF* related to △*F'CF*?

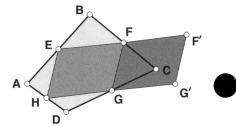

**14.** Explain why the relationship you described in Question 13 must be true.

**15.** How is △*HDG* related to △*G'CG*?

**16.** Explain why the relationship you described in Question 15 must be true.

**17.** How is $\triangle AEH$ related to $\triangle CF'G'$?

**18.** Explain why the relationship you described in Question 17 must be true.

**19.** You have one more triangle to account for. Explain how this last triangle fits into your explanation.

## Present Your Proof

Create a summary of your proof from Questions 10–19. Your summary may be in paper form or electronic form and may include a presentation sketch in Sketchpad. You may want to discuss the summary with your partner or group.

## Further Exploration

Which part of your proof does not work for concave quadrilaterals? Try to redo the proof so that it explains the concave case as well. (*Hint:* Drag point *C* until quadrilateral *ABCD* is concave.)

Sometimes a seemingly correct logical argument can lead to a paradox. Work through the following logical argument in relation to the diagram shown. Do not use Sketchpad yet; you will use it later to check the validity of this argument.

## CONJECTURE

The diagram on the right shows the following construction.

- Triangle *ABC* is any arbitrary triangle.
- $\overline{CG}$ is on the angle bisector of angle *ACB*, and $\overline{GE}$ is the perpendicular bisector of $\overline{AB}$.
- $\overline{GD}$ is perpendicular to $\overline{AC}$, and $\overline{GF}$ is perpendicular to $\overline{BC}$.

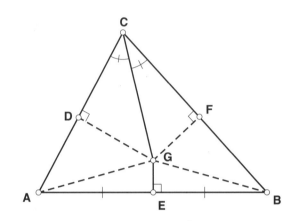

**1.** What can you say about triangles *CGD* and *CGF*? Why?

**2.** From Question 1, what can you conclude about *DG* and *FG*?

**3.** What can you say about *AG* and *BG*? Why?

**4.** What can you now conclude about triangles *GDA* and *GFB*? Why?

**5.** From Question 4, what can you conclude about *DA* and *FB*?

**6.** From Question 1, what can you conclude about *CD* and *CF*?

**7.** What can you now conclude about *CD* + *DA* and *CF* + *FB*, and therefore about *CA* and *CB*?

**8.** From Question 7, what type of triangle is *ABC*?

## REFLECT

Is this argument valid for *any* triangle *ABC*? What is the problem? Where is the mistake? Discuss with your partner or your group.

## CHECK BY CONSTRUCTION

Make an accurate construction in Sketchpad to check the sketch that provides the basis of the logical argument. What do you notice? What important lesson can you learn from this?

To construct an angle bisector, select three points on the angle, making sure the vertex is your middle selection. Then choose **Angle Bisector** from the Construct menu.

To construct a perpendicular, select a point and a straight object. Then choose **Perpendicular Line** from the Construct menu.

© 2003 Key Curriculum Press

# Cyclic Quadrilateral Converse

A cyclic quadrilateral is any quadrilateral that can be circumscribed by a circle.

In your previous work with cyclic quadrilaterals, you have observed that *if a convex quadrilateral is cyclic, its opposite angles* _____ .

In this activity, you will investigate the converse of this statement. Before you go on, write the converse in your own words.

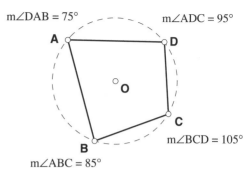

m∠DAB = 75°    m∠ADC = 95°

m∠ABC = 85°    m∠BCD = 105°

## CONJECTURE

☞ Open the sketch **Cyclic Quad.gsp.**

☞ Drag point *D* until ∠*ABC* and ∠*CDA* are supplementary.

☞ Press the button to show the circumcircle of △*ABC*.

    **1.** What do you observe about quadrilateral *ABCD*?

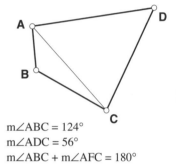

m∠ABC = 124°
m∠ADC = 56°
m∠ABC + m∠AFC = 180°

☞ Press the button to hide the circumcircle of △*ABC*.

☞ Now drag *A*, *B*, or *C* to change the triangle. Repeat the second and third step above. Try this for a few different positions of *A*, *B*, and *C*.

    **2.** Reread the converse statement you wrote at the beginning of this activity. Explain whether your sketch supports or contradicts this statement.

    **3.** How certain are you that your answer in Question 2 is always true? Record your level of certainty on the number line and explain your choice.

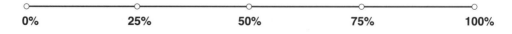

0%          25%          50%          75%          100%

CHALLENGE    If you believe your conjecture is always true, provide some examples to support your view and try to convince your partner or members of your group. Even better, support your conjecture with a logical explanation or a convincing proof. If you suspect your conjecture is not always true, try to supply counterexamples.

## PROVING

You have probably formed the following conjecture:

> If the opposite angles of a convex quadrilateral are supplementary, that quadrilateral is cyclic.

Or alternatively:

> If the two sums of the pairs of opposite angles of a convex quadrilateral are equal, that quadrilateral is cyclic.

You can use a logical argument to verify this conjecture. A logical argument not only supplies us with an understanding of why something is true, but can also help us establish the general validity of a result. A logical argument in mathematics whose purpose is verification is normally called a *proof*.

To continue with a proof of the conjecture, you can use a form of proof called *proof by contradiction*. In this kind of proof, you start by assuming your conclusion is false. Then you show that this leads to a contradiction, indicating that your conclusion must have been true. So we start by assuming that the opposite angles of convex quadrilateral *ABCD* are supplementary, but quadrilateral *ABCD* is *not* cyclic.

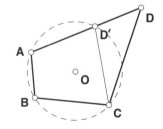

☞ Press the button to construct cyclic quadrilateral *ABCD'*. *D'* is at the intersection of ray *AD* and the circumcircle of triangle *ABC*.

☞ First you will consider the case in which *D* is outside the circle. If *D* is not outside the circle right now, drag vertices in your sketch until this is the case.

**4.** What is the relationship between ∠*ABC* and ∠*AD'C*? Why?

5. What is the *given* relationship between ∠*ABC* and ∠*ADC*? (This relationship does not match the measures in your sketch!)

6. What can you therefore conclude about ∠*ADC* and ∠*AD′C*?

7. Consider the measure of exterior angle *AD′C* of △*DCD′*. Write an expression relating it to the measures of interior angles *ADC* and *DCD′*.

8. Compare your answers to Questions 6 and 7. What can you conclude from this? What does your conclusion imply about *D* and *D′*?

You still need to consider the case in which *D* is inside the circle. Drag *D* until your sketch represents this case.

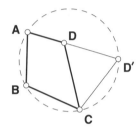

9. Using the same kind of argument, prove that *ABCD* must be cyclic for this case as well. Use another sheet of paper if necessary.

## Present Your Proof

Look over Questions 4–9. Now write a proof of your conjecture in your own words. You may include a demonstration sketch to support and explain your proof.

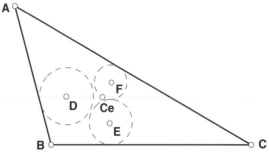

## CONJECTURE

☞ Open the sketch **Concurrency.gsp.** Drag vertices in the sketch to become familiar with it.

**1.** The point *Ce* was constructed to be a special point. Explain what kind of point it is in relation to △*ABC*. Press the buttons in your sketch for hints.

**2.** The three circles in your sketch were also constructed in a special way. Explain what kind of circles they are in relation to △*ABC*. Press the buttons in your sketch for hints.

☞ Construct segments *AE*, *BF*, and *CD*.

**3.** What do you notice about segments *AE*, *BF*, and *CD*? Drag any vertex of △*ABC* to test your conjecture. Make sure to test different-sized triangles. It also helps to hide any medians or interior triangles that are showing.

**4.** How certain are you that your conjecture is always true? Record your level of certainty on the number line and explain your choice.

| 0% | 25% | 50% | 75% | 100% |

**CHALLENGE** If you believe your conjecture is always true, provide some examples to support your view and try to convince your partner or members of your group. Even better, support your conjecture with a logical explanation or a convincing proof. If you suspect your conjecture is not always true, try to supply counterexamples.

© 2003 Key Curriculum Press

You may have previously observed and proved that the *perpendicular bisectors* of the sides of any triangle always intersect in the same point. In this activity, you will make some conjectures about the *altitudes* of a triangle.

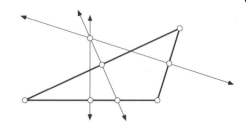

## Sketchpad Accuracy and Certainty

As you may have seen before in the Areas activity, you should be cautious of making a judgment solely on the basis of visual appearance. Even though Sketchpad is very accurate and a powerful tool for visualization, you must still be very careful not to make false conjectures. To ensure that all measurements are set to maximum accuracy, you must look at extreme cases and where possible make use of the enlargement or animation facilities of Sketchpad to check the validity of conjectures. Ultimately, however, only a correct logical explanation/proof can assure absolute certainty.

Note that in everyday life we are often happy to say something is always true, even though we know that there may be occasional exceptions. In mathematics, however, we are only interested in conjectures that are genuinely *always* true. Mathematics is therefore different from everyday life in that absolutely no exceptions are allowed: only *one* counterexample is needed to prove a conjecture false.

# CONJECTURE

☞ Open the sketch **Altitudes.gsp.**

☞ A perpendicular from a vertex of a triangle to its opposite side is called an *altitude.* The point where an altitude meets the opposite side (or its extension) is called its *foot.* Press the buttons in your sketch to show each altitude and foot of $\triangle ABC$.

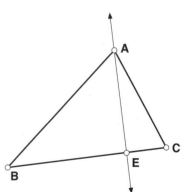

1. Drag any vertex of $\triangle ABC$. What do you notice about the altitudes of a triangle? Check to see if your observations are still true when the triangle is obtuse.

2. **Certainty:** How certain are you that your conjecture from Question 1 is always true? Record your level of certainty on the number line and explain your choice.

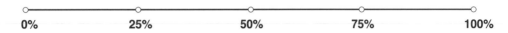

0%        25%        50%        75%        100%

CHALLENGE     If you believe your conjecture is always true, provide some examples to support your view and try to convince your partner or members of your group. Even better, support your conjecture with a logical explanation or a convincing proof. If you suspect your conjecture is not always true, try to supply counterexamples.

## PROVING

Consider the following statement by the mathematician Morris Kline (1985, 11–12):

> *Reasoning by induction and by analogy calls for recourse to observation and even experiment to obtain the facts on which to base each argument. But the senses are limited and inaccurate. Moreover, even if the facts gathered for the purposes of induction and analogy are sound, these methods do not yield unquestionable conclusions. . . .*
>
> *To avoid these sources of error, the mathematician utilizes another method of reasoning . . . in deductive reasoning the conclusion is a logically inescapable consequence of the known facts.*

**3.** Comment on how this quotation from Morris Kline is related to your work on your conjecture.

Now work in the same sketch and use the following arguments to convince yourself of the truth of your original conjecture: *The altitudes of any triangle are concurrent.*

☞ Press the button to show some parallels constructed in your sketch.

To measure the slope of a straight object, select the object and choose **Slope** from the Measure menu.

**4.** The point of concurrency of the altitudes of a triangle is called the *orthocenter.* Drag vertices of △*ABC* as you fill in these blanks:

The altitudes of △*ABC* are _____ , _____ , and _____ .

$\overline{GI}$ is parallel to _____ ,

$\overline{IH}$ is parallel to _____ , and

$\overline{GH}$ is parallel to _____ .

**5.** What can you say about quadrilateral *GBCA*? What type of quadrilateral is it? Why?

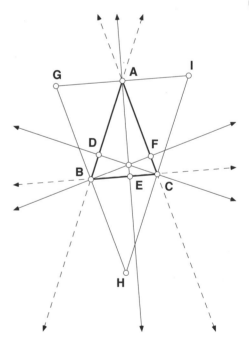

**6.** From Question 5, what can you therefore say about $\overline{GA}$ and $\overline{BC}$?

**7.** What can you say about quadrilateral *ABCI*? What type of quadrilateral is it? Why?

**8.** From Question 7, what can you therefore say about $\overline{AI}$ and $\overline{BC}$?

**9.** From Questions 6 and 8, what can you therefore say about $\overline{GA}$ and $\overline{AI}$?

**10.** What can you say about angles *GAE* and *IAE*? Why?

**11.** Explain why the original construction guarantees your observation from Question 10.

**12.** What type of line is $\overleftrightarrow{AE}$ in relation to $\overline{GI}$?

**13.** Can you say the same thing for line *BF* with respect to $\overline{GH}$, and for line *CD* with respect to $\overline{HI}$?

**14.** From Questions 12 and 13, what can you conclude about lines *AE*, *BF*, and *CD*? Why?

## Presenting Your Proof

Look over Questions 5–14. Now write a proof of your conjecture from Question 1 in your own words. You may include a demonstration sketch to support and explain your proof.

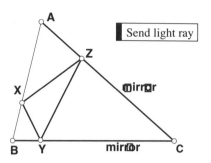

Although this problem is a purely geometric one, it will be easier if you interpret it as a problem in physics. Imagine sitting in a triangular room *ABC* with walls $\overline{BC}$ and $\overline{AC}$ that are mirrors—a little bit like sitting inside a kaleidoscope. A light ray from a laser, sent from a point *X* on $\overline{AB}$ to $\overline{BC}$, reflects from $\overline{BC}$ at *Y* to $\overline{AC}$, and reflects from $\overline{AC}$ at *Z* back to *X*. Where should the light ray start and where should it hit each wall for it to follow the shortest possible path?

## CONJECTURE

✎ Open the sketch **Light Ray.gsp.** Press the button to send the light ray around the triangle.

✎ Press the buttons to show the measures of $\angle XYB$, $\angle ZYC$, $\angle YZC$, $\angle XZA$, $\angle AXZ$, and $\angle BXY$.

   **1.** What do you notice about these angle measures? Check your observations by dragging point *X*.

   **2.** Explain your observation from Question 1 using what you know about light rays.

✎ Drag point *X* along $\overline{AB}$ until the perimeter *XYZ* is a minimum.

✎ Press the button to show each of the three altitudes and their feet.

*If two points overlap, it is possible to drag one point when you want to drag the other point. If this happens, try to select and drag the point again.*

   **3.** What do you notice about the positions of *X*, *Y*, and *Z* in relation to the feet of the altitudes?

✎ Drag any vertex of $\triangle ABC$ to a new position, but keep the triangle acute. Again drag *X* until the perimeter of *XYZ* is a minimum and check your observation in Question 3.

✎ Repeat the preceding step at least one more time.

4. From Questions 1 and 3, what can you conjecture about the pairs of angles at the feet of the altitudes, such as ∠DFA and ∠EFC, ∠FDA and ∠EDB, and ∠DEB and ∠FEC?

☞ Check your conjecture in Question 4 by pressing the button to show the angle measures at the feet of the altitudes.

5. Is your conjecture in Question 4 also true if △ABC is obtuse?

6. **Certainty:** Look back at your conjecture in Question 3 and your conjecture in Question 4. How certain are you that each conjecture is always true? Can you provide convincing proofs or counterexamples to back up your position? Record your level of certainty on the number line and explain your choice.

Conjecture in Question 3:

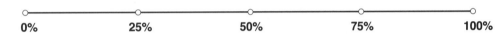

| 0% | 25% | 50% | 75% | 100% |

Conjecture in Question 4:

| 0% | 25% | 50% | 75% | 100% |

**CHALLENGE** If you believe your conjecture is always true, provide some examples to support your view and try to convince your partner or members of your group. Even better, support your conjecture with a logical explanation or a convincing proof. If you suspect your conjecture or your partner's conjecture is not always true, try to supply counterexamples.

## PROVING

You have probably made these two conjectures:

- In acute triangle *ABC*, inscribed triangle *XYZ* has its minimum perimeter when its vertices lie at the feet of the altitudes.

- The pairs of angles surrounding the feet of the altitudes of triangle *ABC* are equal (for example, *m∠DFA = m∠EFC, m∠FDA = m∠EDB,* and *m∠DEB = m∠FEC*).

m∠AXZ = 41°
m∠BXY = 41°

m∠YZC = 76°
m∠XZA = 76°

mirror

mirror

m∠XYB = 63°
m∠ZYC = 63°

But how certain are you? As you may have seen in some earlier experiences, it is possible to draw erroneous conclusions just from observations. For example, conjectures can break down when extreme cases are considered. How do you know that you have checked all possible cases?

Work through the arguments below to convince yourself of the truth of your conjectures. You will prove the second conjecture first.

## PROVING ANGLE MEASURES EQUAL

*To construct an intersection point, select two lines and choose **Intersection** from the Construct menu. To change a label, double-click on the label with the **Text** tool.*

Construct the intersection of the altitudes and label the intersection *O*.

**7.** In quadrilateral *OECF*, what can you say about opposite angles *OEC* and *OFC*? Why?

*To construct an arc, select three vertices in order around the quadrilateral and then choose **Arc Through 3 Points** from the Construct menu. Do this with another set of three points.*

**8.** Use Question 7 to explain why *OECF* is a cyclic quadrilateral (that is, a quadrilateral inscribed in a circle).

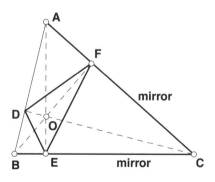

**9.** From Question 8, what can you conclude about ∠*EOC* and ∠*EFC*?

**10.** In quadrilateral *ADOF*, what can you say about opposite angles *ADO* and *AFO*? What type of quadrilateral is *ADOF*, therefore? (Check your conclusion by a construction in Sketchpad, if you like.)

**11.** From Question 10, what can you conclude about ∠*AFD* and ∠*AOD*?

**12.** What can you say about ∠*EOC* and ∠*AOD*? Why?

**13.** What can you therefore conclude from Questions 9, 11, and 12?

**14.** Explain how the same argument applies for the pairs of angles at the other two altitudes.

## PROVING MINIMUM PERIMETER

Now you will prove your first conjecture. Reread your first conjecture, then work carefully through the steps that follow.

☞ Press the buttons to hide the altitudes and all the angle measures.

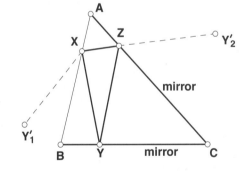

To reflect the point, select segment or line *AB* and choose **Mark Mirror** from the Transform menu. Then select *Y* and choose **Reflect** from the Transform menu.

☞ Reflect *Y* across $\overline{AB}$. Call this point $Y'_1$.

☞ Reflect *Y* across $\overline{AC}$. Call this point $Y'_2$.

☞ Construct $\overline{Y'_1 X}$ and $\overline{Y'_2 Z}$.

**15.** What can you now say about $\overline{XY'_1}$ and $\overline{XY}$, and $\overline{Y'_2 Z}$ and $\overline{ZY}$? Why?

**16.** From Question 15, what can you say about the lengths of the path $XY + YZ + ZX$ and the path $XY'_1 + ZX + ZY'_2$?

**17.** What do you notice about points $X$, $Z$, and $Y'_2$? Try to explain (prove) your observation.

**18.** Drag $X$ until the length of the path $XY'_1 + ZX + ZY'_2$ is a minimum. Explain the location of $X$.

**19.** Show (prove) that if the construction meets the condition in Question 18, then $m\angle AXZ = m\angle BXY$.

**20.** From Question 19 and from the result in the first proving section of this activity, what can you conclude about the position of $\triangle XYZ$ for its perimeter to be a minimum?

## Presenting Your Proof

Summarize one or both of your proofs. Your summaries may be in paper form or electronic form and may include a presentation sketch in Sketchpad. You may want to discuss these summaries with your partner or group.

## Further Exploration

**Historical Note:**
The problem of an inscribed triangle with the smallest perimeter in an acute triangle was first proposed by Hermann Schwarz (1843–1921), a professor at Göttingen in Berlin, Germany, and one of the most distinguished researchers on the calculus of variations in the nineteenth century.

Use your light ray sketch to check cases where $\triangle ABC$ is right or obtuse. Where should you locate $\triangle XYZ$ for it to have minimum perimeter? Try to explain your solution.

## CONJECTURE

☞ Open the sketch **Parallel.gsp.** Drag different points in your sketch. Notice that point $D$ is a free point on $\overline{AB}$ of $\triangle ABC$.

☞ Press the button that draws a segment from point $D$.

**1.** Drag point $D$ and then complete this statement: $\overline{ED}$ _____ $\overline{CA}$.

☞ Press the button that draws a segment from point $E$.

**2.** Drag point $D$ again and then complete this statement: $\overline{EF}$ _____ $\overline{BA}$.

☞ Press the button that draws a segment from point $F$.

**3.** Drag point $D$ again and then complete this statement: $\overline{FG}$ _____ $\overline{BC}$.

**4.** Make sure that points $D$ and $G$ are not overlapping. Do you think you would ever come back to your starting point $D$ if you continued drawing parallel segments to the sides?

If you don't think you would come back to your starting point $D$, why not? If you think you would, under what conditions, and after drawing how many parallel segments?

☞ Construct at least another three parallel lines continuing the pattern of the first three segments.

To construct your first parallel line, select point $G$, then $\overline{AC}$, and choose **Parallel Line** from the Construct menu.

**5.** What do you notice? Drag point $D$ and any of the vertices of $\triangle ABC$ to check your observation.

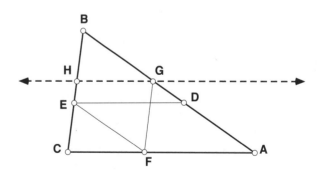

**6.** How certain are you that your conjecture is always true? Record your level of certainty on the number line and explain your choice.

0%        25%        50%        75%        100%

CHALLENGE    If you believe your conjecture is always true, provide some examples to support your view and try to convince your partner or members of your group. Even better, support your conjecture with a logical explanation or a convincing proof. If you suspect your conjecture is not always true, try to supply counterexamples.

## ● PROVING

You should have noticed that if you construct
parallel lines as described, you need to go
around only twice (constructing a total of six
parallel lines) before you return to your starting
point $D$. (When $D$ is at the midpoint of $\overline{AB}$, you
need to go around only once, constructing three
parallel lines.) Most people find this surprising,
thinking instead that in some instances you
might never return to the beginning. How can
we convince ourselves that this is *always* the case?

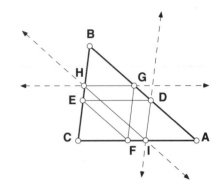

☞ Press the button to show the ratios $\frac{BD}{DA}$ and $\frac{BE}{EC}$.

**7.** Drag point $D$ and any vertex of $\triangle ABC$ to look for patterns. What do
you notice about these ratios? This will show a pattern in a triangle
that you may already have proved or discovered.

● You will use your results from Question 7 in the rest of your proof.

To continue with a proof of your original
conjecture from Question 5, you can
use a form of proof called *proof by
contradiction.* To use proof by
contradiction, start by assuming that
your conclusion is false. Then show that
this leads to a contradiction. In this
activity, assume that you do not return
to point $D$ after constructing six parallels.
Assume instead that you return to some
different point $J$, as in the picture. Otherwise, the picture matches your
construction so far: $\overline{DE} \parallel \overline{GH} \parallel \overline{AC}$, $\overline{FG} \parallel \overline{IJ} \parallel \overline{CB}$, and $\overline{FE} \parallel \overline{IH} \parallel \overline{AB}$. Can
you now logically show that $J$ *must* coincide with $D$?

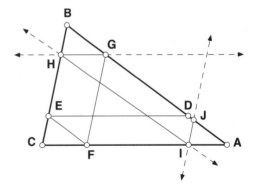

First try it on your own, but if you get stuck, read and work through the
following for planning a possible proof.

**8.** Use your result from Question 7 to continue the sequence of equations relating all the ratios into which the sides are divided by the points $D$, $E$, $F$, $G$, $H$, $I$, and $J$.

$$\frac{BD}{DA} = \frac{BE}{EC} = \frac{AF}{FC} = \underline{\hspace{3cm}}$$

**9.** What do your equations say about $\frac{AD}{DB}$ and $\frac{AJ}{JB}$? What can you conclude from this?

## Presenting Your Proof

Look over Questions 7–9. Now write a proof of your conjecture in your own words. You may include a demonstration sketch to support and explain your proof.

## Further Exploration

**1.** What happens if one or more of the points $D$ through $I$ fall on the extensions of $\overline{AB}$, $\overline{BC}$, and $\overline{AC}$? Does your result still hold?

**2.** What happens if in a pentagon $ABCDE$, a segment $FG$ is drawn parallel to $\overline{AC}$ from a point $F$ on $\overline{AB}$, a segment $GH$ is drawn parallel to $\overline{BD}$, and so on? Would we ever come back to point $F$? Prove your observations.

**3.** Generalize your observation in Question 2 to polygons with a similar property.

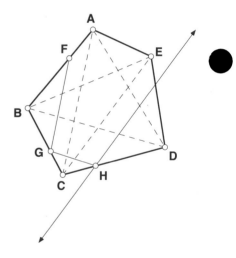

# 4

# Proof as

## Challenge

# Parallelogram Angle Bisectors

In this activity, you will investigate the kind of quadrilateral formed by the angle bisectors of a parallelogram.

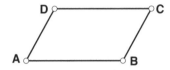

## CONJECTURE

👉 Open the sketch **Parallelogram.gsp.**

**1.** Drag different vertices of your quadrilateral *ABCD*. What features of quadrilateral *ABCD* make you sure it is a parallelogram? Take measurements if you wish.

👉 Press the buttons that show each of the four angle bisectors of parallelogram *ABCD*.

👉 Press the button that shows the quadrilateral formed by the intersection of the angle bisectors.

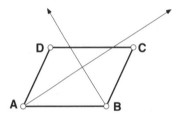

**2.** Drag different vertices of quadrilateral *ABCD*. What kind of quadrilateral do you think *EFGH* is? (Measure its angles if necessary.)

**3.** Try to drag vertices of *ABCD* until all sides of *EFGH* are equal. What do you find?

**4.** What happens to *EFGH* when *ABCD* is a square?

**5.** What happens to *EFGH* when *ABCD* is a rhombus?

**CHALLENGE**    Provide proofs of your conjectures from Questions 2–5 above.

## PROVING

In the preceding section, you constructed the angle bisectors of a parallelogram, then formed quadrilateral *EFGH* at the intersections of the bisectors. You should have found that

- *EFGH* is always a rectangle. (Sometimes *EFGH* is a square, which is a special case of a rectangle, and sometimes *EFGH* is a point, which you can think of as a rectangle with sides of length 0.)

- *EFGH* is a square only when *ABCD* is a rectangle. However, when *ABCD* is a square or a rhombus, the angle bisectors meet in one point.

The hints that follow will help you prove these observations.

## PROVING *EFGH* IS A RECTANGLE

**6.** Let $m\angle DAB = 2x$ and $m\angle ABC = 2y$. Express $m\angle AHG$ in terms of $x$ and $y$.

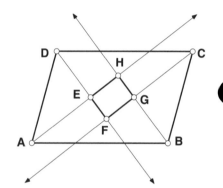

**7.** What can you say about the sum of the measures of angles *DAB* and *ABC*? Why?

**8.** Write your observation from Question 7 as an expression in terms of $x$ and $y$ and simplify.

**9.** How is Question 8 related to Question 6? What does this tell you about $m\angle AHG$?

**10.** Explain whether the same argument applies to the other angles of *EFGH*.

## PROVING *EFGH* IS A SQUARE WHEN *ABCD* IS A RECTANGLE

**11.** When *ABCD* is a rectangle, what can you say
about $\overline{FD}$ and $\overline{FC}$? Why?

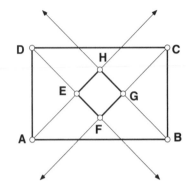

**12.** What can you say about triangles *DAE* and
*CBG*? Why?

**13.** What does this imply regarding $\overline{ED}$ and $\overline{GC}$?

**14.** From Questions 11–13, what can you therefore say about $\overline{FE}$
and $\overline{FG}$? Why?

**15.** What does this tell you about *EFGH*?

### Further Exploration

**1.** Explain why rectangle *EFGH* is a point only when *ABCD* is a rhombus.

**2.** In a new sketch, construct the angle bisectors of any quadrilateral and
investigate the type of quadrilateral they form. Prove your observations.

In this activity, you will investigate the kind of quadrilateral formed by connecting points *E, F, G,* and *H* in the construction shown here. The construction contains special quadrilaterals.

## CONJECTURE

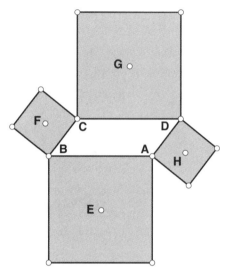

☞ Open the sketch **Para Squares.gsp.** Drag points in your sketch to familiarize yourself with this construction.

1. Describe the four shaded quadrilaterals.

2. Describe quadrilateral *ABCD*.

☞ Use the **Segment** tool to construct quadrilateral *EFGH*.

3. Drag any of the points *A, B, C,* and *D*. What kind of quadrilateral is *EFGH*? Measure some angles and sides to check your conjecture.

4. Drag *A* so that $\overline{AD}$ is parallel to $\overline{AB}$. Does your conjecture from Question 3 still hold?

5. Drag *A* across $\overline{CD}$ so that the shaded quadrilaterals overlap. Does your conjecture from Question 3 still hold?

CHALLENGE    Provide a proof of your conjecture from Question 3.

## Investigating Further

You have observed that quadrilateral *EFGH* is always a square, but you may not yet be able to explain *why* this is true. This section will help you investigate the problem further to come up with some ideas for a proof.

☛ Press the *Half-turn* button.

**6.** What do you notice about the original construction? Describe its symmetry. Since a quadrilateral *EFGH* has the same symmetry, what can you already conclude about it?

☛ Press the button that shows triangles *HAE* and *HDG*.

**7.** What do you notice about these two triangles? Drag points and take measurements to explore experimentally. Then try to explain your observations logically.

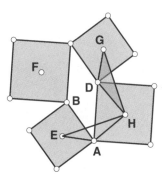

Carefully select the interior and choose **Rotate** from the Transform menu. Type the number of degrees you wish to rotate and click OK.

☛ Double-click on point *H* to mark it as a center of rotation. Then rotate the interior of △*HDG* so that it lies inside △*HAE*.

**8.** How many degrees did you rotate around *H* to map △*HDG* onto △*HAE*?

**9.** What can you now conclude regarding ∠*EHG*, and consequently about *EFGH*?

CHALLENGE    Try to use your observations from Questions 6–9 to construct a proof that quadrilateral *EFGH* is a square. Discuss your thoughts with a partner. If you get stuck, read the hints that follow.

## PROVING

The development of a logical argument to defend a mathematical result is often perceived as an intellectual challenge by mathematicians. This is your chance to rise to that challenge!

Follow the steps below to construct a proof of your original conjecture.

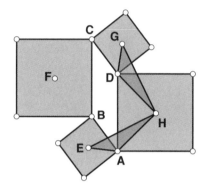

**10.** Explain the relationship between $\angle HAE$ and $\angle BAD$. (*Hint:* Drag point $B$ until $\overline{AB}$ is parallel to $\overline{AD}$.)

**11.** Explain the relationship between $\angle BAD$ and $\angle ADC$.

**12.** Describe $\angle HDG$ in terms of $\angle BAD$. (*Hint:* Look at the angles surrounding point $D$.)

**13.** What can you conclude from Questions 11 and 12?

**14.** What can you say about the corresponding sides $EA$ and $GD$ of triangles $HAE$ and $HDG$? Why?

**15.** What can you say about the corresponding sides $AH$ and $DH$? Why?

**16.** From Questions 13–15, what can you conclude about triangles $HAE$ and $HDG$, and therefore about the corresponding sides $HE$ and $HG$?

**17.** What can you conclude about quadrilateral $EFGH$ at this point?

**18.** What can you say about $\angle AHD$? Why?

**19.** What can you therefore say about ∠*EHG*? Why?

**20.** What can you conclude about quadrilateral *EFGH* now? Why?

## Present Your Proof

Look over Questions 6 and 10–20. Now write a proof of your original conjecture in your own words. You may include a demonstration sketch to support and explain your proof.

## Further Exploration

**1.** In Question 5, you saw that if the squares lie inwardly and overlap (rather than lying outwardly), the result still holds. Can you adapt your proof for this configuration?

**2.** What type of quadrilateral is formed by the centers of squares constructed on the sides of an isosceles trapezoid? Can you explain your observation?

**3.** What type of quadrilateral is formed by the centers of the squares constructed on the sides of a kite?

In this investigation, you'll make and prove some conjectures about a right triangle.

## CONJECTURE

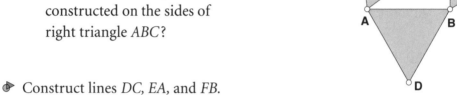

👉 Open the sketch **Fermat 1.gsp.** Drag any vertex to investigate the shapes in the sketch.

1. What kind of triangles are constructed on the sides of right triangle *ABC*?

👉 Construct lines *DC*, *EA*, and *FB*.

2. What do you notice about these lines? Drag any vertex of △*ABC* to test your observations.

To measure the distance between two points, select both points and choose **Distance** from the Measure menu.

👉 Measure the distances *DC*, *EA*, and *FB*.

3. What do you notice about these distances? Carefully check your observations by further dragging.

4. Drag *C* past *B*. What happens to the triangles?

5. When you drag *C* past *B*, do your observations from Questions 2 and 3 still hold?

CHALLENGE    Provide proofs of your conjectures from Questions 2, 3, and 5 above.

## VERIFYING

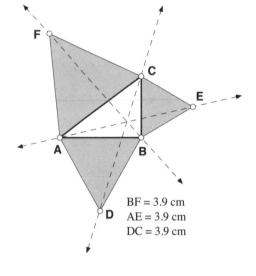

*Perhaps, though, there is another purpose to proof—as a testing ground for the stamina and ingenuity of the mathematician. We admire the conqueror of Everest, not because the top of Everest is a place we want to be, but just because it is so hard to get there.*

*—Davis and Hersh, 1983*

BF = 3.9 cm
AE = 3.9 cm
DC = 3.9 cm

You have noticed that if equilateral triangles *DBA*, *ECB*, and *FAC* are constructed on the sides of any right triangle *ABC*,

- The lines *DC*, *EA*, and *FB* are concurrent.
- Segments *DC*, *EA*, and *FB* are equal in length.

What is more, this result appears to be true even if the triangles lie inwardly. This point of concurrency is known as the Fermat-Torricelli point. (The mathematicians Pierre de Fermat and Evangelista Torricelli discovered it independently of each other.)

But how do we know our conjectures are really true? As you may have seen in the activity Concurrency, we must be careful not to form conclusions too easily. Let us investigate the problem further to come up with some ideas for a proof.

☞ Press the button that shows the interior of △*DBC*.

☞ Press the button that rotates the interior of △*DBC* around point *B* by −60°.

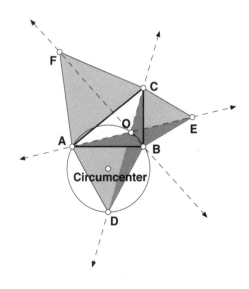

Circumcenter

   **6.** What do you notice about the rotated triangle? Try to find other pairs of triangles.

To construct a point at the intersection of three lines, select two of them and choose **Intersection** from the Construct menu.

To measure an angle, select three points on the angle, making sure the vertex is the middle selection. Then choose **Distance** from the Measure menu.

☞ Construct a point at the point of concurrency and label it *O*.

☞ Next, measure the six angles formed around point *O*.

**7.** What do you notice about the six angles around *O*? Drag a vertex of △*ABC* to check your observations.

☞ Show the circumcircle of △*ADB*.

**8.** What relationship is there between ∠*AOB* and ∠*ADB*? What can you conclude from that? (*Hint:* Look at quadrilateral *AOBD*.)

**9.** Press the button that shows all the circumcircles and circumcenters of the equilateral triangles. Look at the other two triangles. What do you notice?

CHALLENGE       Try to use your observations from Questions 6–9 to construct a proof that *AE* = *BF* = *DC*, as well as that lines *AE*, *BF*, and *DC* are concurrent. Discuss your thoughts with a partner. If you get stuck, read the hints that follow.

## PROVING SEGMENTS EQUAL

Here are some hints for planning a possible proof of this conjecture:

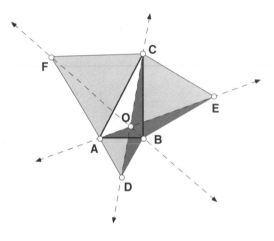

> If equilateral triangles *DBA*, *ECB*, and *FAC* are constructed on the sides of any right triangle *ABC*, then the lengths *DC*, *EA*, and *FB* are equal.

☞ It will help if you hide the circumcircles and circumcenters. You don't need to hide triangles *DBC* and *ABE*, but remember that they are not part of the original construction.

**10.** In triangles *DBC* and *ABE*, what can you say about corresponding sides *DB* and *AB*? Why?

**11.** What can you say about corresponding sides *BC* and *BE*? Why?

**12.** What can you say about corresponding angles *DBC* and *ABE*? Why?

**13.** What can you therefore conclude about triangles *DBC* and *ABE*?

**14.** From Question 13, what can you conclude about corresponding sides *DC* and *AE*?

**15.** Repeat the above for triangles *EAC* and *BFC* to complete the proof.

**16.** Did your answers to any of the Questions 10–15 use the fact that ∠*ABC* measures 90°? What does that imply about the conjecture you just proved?

**17.** Consider the quotation below in relation to your conclusion in Question 16.

> *A good proof should convey an insight into exactly why the proposition is true. Such insight sometimes reveals the pleasant, unanticipated surprise that the proposition is merely a special case of a more general one, thus allowing for its immediate generalization.*
>
> —*M. D. de Villiers, 1998*

In what way has your proof provided you with insight that led to an immediate generalization?

## PROVING LINES CONCURRENT

Here are some hints for planning a possible proof of your second conjecture:

If equilateral triangles *DBA*, *ECB*, and *FAC* are constructed on the sides of any right triangle *ABC*, the lines *DC*, *EA*, and *FB* are concurrent.

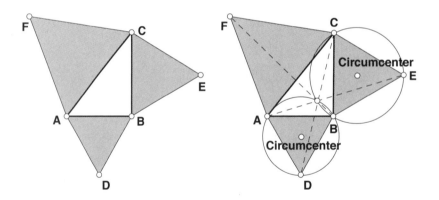

☞ Hide point *O* and the lines *BF*, *DC*, and *AE*.

☞ Press the button that hides triangles *DBC* and *ABE*.

☞ Press the button that shows circumcircles *ADB* and *BEC*. They should intersect at point *B*.

☞ Construct the other point of intersection of these two circles. This will be your new point *O*.

☞ Use the **Segment** tool (not the **Line** tool) to construct the six segments *OA*, *OB*, *OC*, *OD*, *OE*, and *OF*.

We will first prove that *AOE* and *DOC* are straight lines and then that the circumcircle *AFC* also passes through *O*. Using this fact, we will then show that *BOF* is also a straight line, which implies that $\overline{AE}$, $\overline{DC}$, and $\overline{BF}$ are concurrent at *O*. (*Note:* We *cannot* assume that lines *AOE*, *DOC*, and *BOF* are straight because that is what we need to prove.)

18. What can you say about the measure of angle *BCE*? Why?

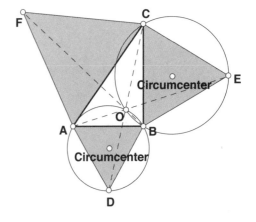

19. From Question 18, what can you now say about the measure of angle *BOE*? Why?

20. What can you say about the measure of angle *BOA*? Why?

21. From Questions 19 and 20, what can you now conclude about angle *AOE*?

22. Repeat the same argument to show that *DOC* is a straight line.

23. From the angles determined above, calculate the measure of angle *AOC*.

24. From Question 23, what can you now conclude about quadrilateral *CFAO*? Why?

☞ Press the button to show circumcircle *AFC* and check your result from Question 24.

25. Repeat the same argument as in Questions 18–21 to show that *BOF* is a straight line.

**26.** Would the preceding argument still be valid if $m\angle ABC$ were not 90°? What can you conclude from that?

**27.** Consider the quotation below, from a Russian mathematician, in relation to your conclusion in Question 26.

*A good proof is one that makes us wiser.*

—*Yu Manin, 1981*

In what way has the proof made you "wiser"?

☞ Open the sketch **Fermat 2.gsp** and use it to check your conclusions in Questions 24 and 26.

## Present Your Proofs

Create summaries of one or both of your proofs for any triangle. Your summaries may be in paper form or electronic form and may include a presentation sketch in Sketchpad. You may want to discuss these summaries with your partner or group.

## Further Exploration

Can you find arrangements of similar or other triangles on the sides of any triangle *ABC* such that one or both of your results also hold?

Suppose an airport is planned to service three cities of approximately equal size. The planners decide to locate the airport so that the sum of the distances to the three cities is a minimum. Where should the airport be located?

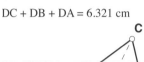

DC = 2.006 cm

DB = 1.663 cm

DA = 2.653 cm

DC + DB + DA = 6.321 cm

## CONJECTURE

☞ Open the sketch **Airport.gsp.**

☞ Drag point $D$ until the sum of the distances to the three cities is a minimum. Search patiently and logically.

☞ What are the measures of angles $ADC$, $BDA$, and $CDB$?

**1.** What do you notice about these three angles?

☞ Drag $A$, $B$, or $C$ to a different position, but make sure $\triangle ABC$ remains acute. Again, drag $D$ to obtain the optimal point for this new triangle.

**2.** Compare the new measurements of angles $ADC$, $BDA$, and $CDB$ with those in Question 1. What do you notice?

**3.** Use your observations to write a conjecture.

**4. Certainty:** How certain are you that your conjecture is always true? Record your level of certainty on the number line and explain your choice.

| 0% | 25% | 50% | 75% | 100% |

**CHALLENGE**    If you believe your conjecture is always true, provide some examples to support your view and try to convince your partner or members of your group. Even better, support your conjecture with a logical explanation or a convincing proof. If you suspect your conjecture or your partner's conjecture is not always true, try to supply counterexamples.

© 2003 Key Curriculum Press

## PROVING

In the preceding section, you should have found that the optimal position for the airport in acute triangle *ABC* appears to be at a point connected to the vertices by lines that make angles of approximately 120°. But how certain are you?

Work through the argument below to convince yourself of your conjecture. It relies on the construction of an equivalent problem in which the optimal position is easier to locate. Follow along in your sketch if you like.

◈ Drag *D* to a new point inside △*ABC*.

◈ Press the button in your sketch that rotates △*ADC* by −60° around point *C* to get △*A'D'C*.

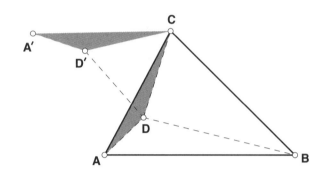

**5.** From the rotation, what can you conclude about the lengths of $\overline{CD}$ and $\overline{CD'}$?

**6.** What type of triangle is triangle *DCD'*? (*Hint:* Use the fact that angle *D'CD* measures 60° and your conclusion in Question 5.)

**7.** From Question 6, what can you conclude about the lengths of $\overline{D'D}$ and $\overline{DC}$?

**8.** From the rotation, what can you conclude about the lengths of $\overline{AD}$ and $\overline{A'D'}$? Why?

**9.** What can you now conclude regarding $AD + CD + BD$ and $A'D' + D'D + DB$?

**10.** When will the path from $A'$ to $B$ ($A'D' + D'D + DB$) be a minimum?

⟳ Drag *D* until your sketch meets the condition in Question 10. (*Hint:* It may help to construct $\overline{A'B}$.)

**11.** When the condition in Question 10 is met, what can you conclude about the size of angle *A'D'C*, and therefore also about angle *ADC*?

**12.** Explain how by rotating △*CDB* by −60° you can prove that angle *CDB* measures 120°.

## Looking Back

You may have noticed earlier that the optimal point for the airport is the Fermat-Torricelli point, discussed in the preceding activity. Show that the construction in this activity is equivalent to constructing equilateral triangles *A'AC*, *B'BA*, and *C'CB* on the sides of △*ABC* (see the diagram) and constructing *A'B*, *B'C*, and *C'A* to meet at *D*.

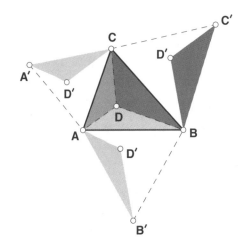

## Historical Notes

Versions of the "airport problem" and its associated geometric properties have been studied by dozens of mathematicians for the last 300 years (even though they didn't have aircraft 300 years ago!). Pierre de Fermat appears to have first posed the airport problem in an essay on optimization. He wanted to find a point inside an acute triangle such that the sum of the distances to the three vertices is a minimum. Fermat was born in 1601 and was a lawyer by profession. Although mathematics was simply an interesting hobby to him, he made important contributions to number theory, analytic geometry, calculus, and probability theory.

The Italian mathematician and scientist Evangelista Torricelli proposed constructing equilateral triangles on the sides of any triangle to locate the optimal point (see the preceding activity The Fermat-Torricelli Point). Although this solution was proposed in 1640, it was published in 1659 by Viviani, one of Torricelli's students. Torricelli is probably better known for his research into the nature of gas, which led to the invention of the mercury barometer.

The solution described in this activity was more recently invented in 1929 by the German mathematician J. Hoffman. Several other famous mathematicians—for example, C. F. Gauss and J. Steiner— have investigated the problem and have produced some interesting generalizations.

## Further Exploration

1. The dynamic Sketchpad sketch of the three cities is an example of a mathematical model that can be used to represent and analyze real-world situations. However, real-world situations are extremely complex and usually have to be simplified before mathematics can be meaningfully applied to them. What are some of the assumptions that could have been made to simplify the original problem?

2. Can you relate the airport problem to the result discovered and proven in the activity Distances in an Equilateral Triangle, and use it to develop a kind of indirect proof for the optimal placement of the airport? (Use the sketch **Airport 2.gsp** to investigate the relationship.)

3. Where should the airport be placed if the cities lie in the shape of an obtuse triangle with one of the angles greater than 120°?

4. Where should the airport be placed if the three cities all lie in a straight line (are collinear)? Can you generalize?

5. Where should the airport be placed if the cities are all of different sizes, for example, if A, B, and C respectively have 60,000, 100,000, and 70,000 people?

6. Where should the airport be placed if there are four cities instead of only three? (Use the sketch **Airport 5.gsp** to investigate the problem.) Is your solution also valid if the four cities lie in the shape of a concave quadrilateral?

7. Where should a spaceport be built for four planets that lie in the shape of a tetrahedron so that the total sum of distances from the spaceport to the planets is a minimum?

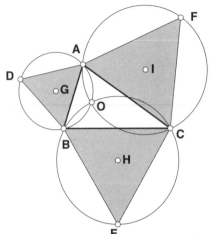

If you construct equilateral triangles on the sides of any triangle, you get some interesting results. You may have already discovered some of these if you worked through the previous activity The Fermat-Torricelli Point. One result this activity requires is that the three circumcircles of the equilateral triangles are always concurrent at a special point, called the Fermat-Torricelli point. This point is labeled *O* in the diagram.

In this activity, you'll discover another result related to this construction, attributed to Napoleon Bonaparte, the famous French emperor and general. Napoleon greatly enjoyed geometry and apparently discovered and proved this next conjecture.

## CONJECTURE

☞ Open the sketch **Napoleon.gsp.** Drag different points in your sketch to become familiar with the construction.

☞ Use the **Segment** tool to connect the centers *G*, *H*, and *I*.

1. Drag any vertex of △*ABC*. What do you notice about △*GHI*? Take measurements if necessary and drag some more to confirm your conjecture.

2. Check your conjecture from Question 1 for the following special cases:

• Triangle *ABC* is obtuse.

• Points *A*, *B*, and *C* lie on the same line.

• The equilateral triangles lie inwardly and overlap.

Report your observations.

CHALLENGE Try to prove your conjecture from Question 1. (*Hints:* (1) Construct $\overline{AO}$, $\overline{BO}$, and $\overline{CO}$ and consider their relationship to the sides of △*GHI*. (2) Use the results proved in the activity The Fermat-Torricelli Point.) If you get stuck, go on to the more detailed hints that follow.

## PROVING

In the preceding section, you should have found this surprising result:

If you construct equilateral triangles on each side of a triangle and then connect their centers, you form another equilateral triangle.

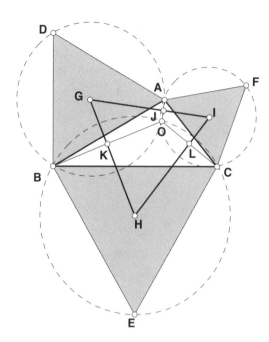

Below are some hints for planning a possible proof. Read and work through them carefully.

In previous work, we have already proved that the three circumcircles meet at the Fermat-Torricelli point $O$. We will now use the properties of cyclic quadrilaterals to show that each angle of $\Delta GHI$ measures 60°.

☞ Press the button that shows segments $AO$, $BO$, and $CO$ and their intersections with the sides of $\Delta GHI$.

Press the buttons in your sketch as necessary to see the quadrilaterals in the next few questions more clearly. The buttons eventually hide the quadrilaterals to keep your sketch from getting cluttered.

**3.** What type of quadrilateral is $ADBO$? Why?

**4.** From Question 3, what can you conclude about the measure of angle $AOB$? Why?

**5.** What type of quadrilateral is $GBHO$? Why?

**6.** From Question 5, what can you now conclude about the measure of angle $GKO$? Why?

**7.** What type of quadrilateral is *GOIA*? Why?

**8.** From Question 7, what can you now conclude about the measure of angle *GJO*? Why?

**9.** What can you now conclude about angle *KGJ* in quadrilateral *GJOK*? Why?

**10.** Repeat Questions 3–9 for either of the other two angles of △*GHI*.

## Present Your Proof

Look over Questions 3–10. Now write a proof of your original conjecture in your own words. You may include a demonstration sketch to support and explain your proof.

## Further Exploration

Investigate what happens to △*GHI* if different arrangements of similar triangles are placed on the sides of △*ABC*.

In this investigation, you will explore a
construction based on arbitrary points
on the sides of an arbitrary triangle and
some circles related to these points. The
result you will find was apparently first
discovered by a French mathematician
named Auguste Miquel in 1838.

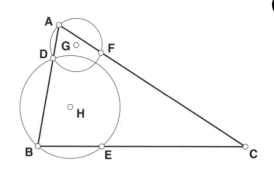

## CONJECTURE

⬧ Open the sketch **Miquel.gsp.** Drag different points to familiarize yourself
with the sketch.

**1.** Explain the locations of points *G* and *H*.

⬧ Press the button to show the circle through the points *F*, *E*, and *C* and its
center *I*.

**2.** What do you notice about the three circles?

⬧ Drag any of the points *D*, *E*, and *F* to check or change your observation.

⬧ Also change the shape of △*ABC* by dragging any vertex to check or change
your observation.

⬧ Press the button to show △*GHI*.

To find the ratio between
two segment lengths,
select both segments,
then choose **Ratio** from
the Measure menu.

**3.** Drag point *A*, *B*, or *C*. What do you notice about the shape of △*GHI*?
(Take measurements, if necessary, to confirm your guess.)

⬧ Drag point *D*, *E*, or *F* to check or change your observation.

⬧ Also change the shape of △*ABC* by dragging any vertex to check or change
your observation in Question 3.

CHALLENGE    Can you prove either of your conjectures from Question 2 and
Question 3? (*Hint:* Use the property that a cyclic quadrilateral—
a convex quadrilateral inscribed in a circle—has opposite angles
that are supplementary.)

# ● PROVING

You should have found the surprising results that the three circles are always concurrent at a point and the centers *G*, *H*, and *I* form a triangle similar to △*ABC*. We can state these two separate conjectures in the following way.

If three points *D*, *E*, and *F* are constructed on the sides of any triangle *ABC*, with *D* on $\overline{AB}$, *E* on $\overline{BC}$, and *F* on $\overline{CA}$, then

- The circumcircles of triangles *ADF*, *BDE*, and *CEF* are concurrent.
- The circumcircles of triangles *ADF*, *BDE*, and *CEF* form a triangle similar to △*ABC*.

The hints that follow will help you prove these observations. Read and work through them carefully.

## PROVING CIRCUMCIRCLES CONCURRENT

☞ Press the button that hides circle *FEC*.

☞ Press the button that shows segments *OD*, *OE*, and *OF* as well as points *J* and *K*.

☞ Press the button that hides △*GHI*.

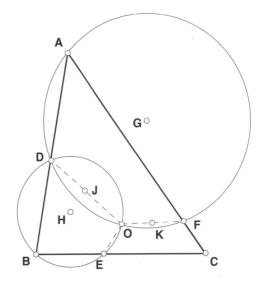

We will first prove that quadrilateral *OECF* is cyclic, which implies that the three circles *ADF*, *BDE*, and *CEF* are concurrent at *O*.

**4.** Express the measure of angle *DOF* in terms of the measure of angle *A*. Give a reason for your equation.

**5.** Express the measure of angle *DOE* in terms of the measure of angle *B*. Give a reason for your equation.

**6.** Using Questions 4 and 5, determine the measure of angle *EOF*. Give a reason.

**7.** Use Question 6 and your knowledge of the sum of the angle measures of a triangle to express the measure of angle *EOF* in terms of the measure of angle *C*.

**8.** From Question 7 and your knowledge of the sum of the angle measures of a triangle, what can you now conclude about quadrilateral *OECF*? Why?

## PROVING TRIANGLE *GHI* SIMILAR TO TRIANGLE *ABC*

Now you will prove your second conjecture. Use the buttons in your sketch to show the quadrilaterals as you need them in this next section. The quadrilaterals blink, but then eventually remain hidden so as not to clutter your sketch.

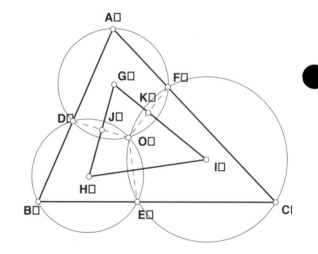

 Show △*GHI*.

**9.** What type of quadrilateral is *GDHO*? Why?

**10.** From Question 9, what can you now say about ∠*GJO*? Why?

**11.** What type of quadrilateral is *GOIF*? Why?

**12.** From Question 11, what can you now say about ∠*GKO*? Why?

**13.** From Questions 10 and 12, what can you conclude about quadrilateral *GJOK*? Why?

**14.** From Question 4 in the previous proof, and Question 13 on the previous page, what can you now conclude regarding ∠*JGK*? Why?

**15.** Repeat Questions 9–14 for either of the other angles of Δ*GHI*.

## Present Your Proofs

Look over the steps for both proofs above. Now write a proof of one or both conjectures in your own words. You may include a demonstration sketch to support and explain each proof.

## Investigate Further

**1.** Investigate what happens if point *D* lies on line *AB* but not necessarily between *A* and *B*. Are the results still valid if one or more of the points *D*, *E*, and *F* fall on extensions of the sides of Δ*ABC*?

**2.** Start with an arbitrary point *O* in a triangle *ABC* and construct lines to make equal angles with the sides as shown below. (Use the sketch **Miquel 2.gsp.**) What conjectures can you make and prove?

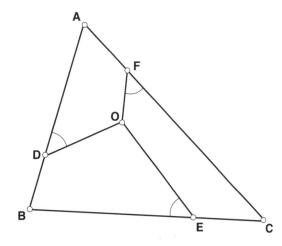

# 5

# Proof as

## Systematization

In the activities Isosceles Trapezoid and Kite Midpoints, to explain (prove) our conjectures, we used the result that the midpoints of two sides of a triangle form a segment that is parallel to the third side and half its length. But why is this result true? Can we also prove it?

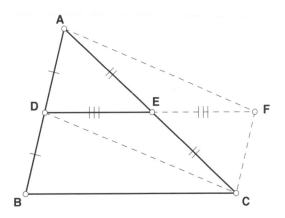

## PROVING

Here are some hints for planning a possible proof. Read and work through them if you want or try to construct your own proof. If necessary, open the sketch **Triangle Midpoints.gsp** to help you answer the questions that follow.

Consider the figure above where it is given that $AD = DB$ and $AE = EC$. Extend $\overline{DE}$ to $F$ so that $DE = EF$. Connect $A$ and $C$ with $F$, and $D$ with $C$.

1. What can you conclude about quad $ADCF$? Why?

2. From Question 1, what can you conclude about $\overline{FC}$ and $\overline{AD}$?

3. From Question 2, what can you conclude about $\overline{FC}$ and $\overline{DB}$, and therefore about quad $DBCF$?

4. From Question 3, what can you conclude about $\overline{DF}$ and $\overline{BC}$, and therefore about $\overline{DE}$ and $\overline{BC}$?

## Present Your Proof

Write out your explanation in a clear, systematic way, giving reasons for each step, and be ready to present it to the rest of the class.

## Further Exploration

What is the converse of the theorem you just proved? Formulate it below and use Sketchpad to investigate whether it is true or not, producing a proof or a counterexample.

In the Parallel Lines activity, we used the result that a line parallel to one side of a triangle divides the other two sides in the same ratio. But why is this result true? Can we also prove it?

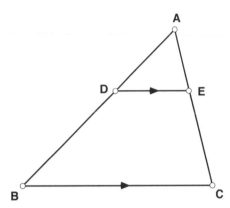

## PROVING

Here are some hints for planning a proof. Read and work through them carefully. Consider the figure above, where it is given that $\overline{DE}$ is parallel to $\overline{BC}$.

**1.** What can you say about angles *ADE* and *ABC*? Why?

**2.** What can you now say about triangles *ABC* and *ADE*? Why?

**3.** From Question 2, what can you conclude about the ratio $\frac{AB}{AD}$ in relation to the ratio $\frac{AC}{AE}$?

**4.** Rewrite the proportion in Question 3, substituting *AD* + *DB* for *AB* and *AE* + *EC* for *AC*.

**5.** From Questions 3 and 4, what can you now conclude about the ratio $\frac{DB}{AD}$ in relation to the ratio $\frac{EC}{AE}$? Why?

**6.** What happens if *D* is the midpoint of side *AB*? How is this related to the theorem proved in the Triangle Midpoints activity?

## Present Your Proof

Write out your proof in a clear, systematic way, giving reasons for each step, and be ready to present it to the rest of the class.

## Further Exploration

What is the converse of the theorem you just proved? Formulate it below and use Sketchpad to investigate whether it is true or not, producing a proof or a counterexample.

# Systematizing Rhombus Properties

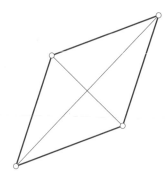

You have earlier discovered or learned that, among others, a rhombus has the following properties:

- All sides are equal.
- The diagonals are perpendicular.
- The diagonals bisect each other.
- There are two axes of symmetry (through the two pairs of opposite angles).
- Opposite sides are parallel.

## DESCRIBE

How would you describe what a rhombus is, over the telephone, to someone who is not yet acquainted with a rhombus?

1. Which of the following descriptions do you think you would be able to use? Circle these descriptions.

   a. A rhombus is any quadrilateral with opposite sides parallel.

   b. A rhombus is any quadrilateral with perpendicular diagonals.

   c. A rhombus is any quadrilateral with two perpendicular axes of symmetry (each through a pair of opposite angles).

   d. A rhombus is any quadrilateral with perpendicular, bisecting diagonals.

   e. A rhombus is any quadrilateral with two pairs of adjacent sides equal.

   f. A rhombus is any quadrilateral with all sides equal.

   g. A rhombus is any quadrilateral with one pair of adjacent sides equal, and opposite sides parallel.

One way of testing a description is to construct a figure complying with the description to see if it really gives the desired figure.

**2.** Open the sketch **Rhombus.gsp** and check each of the descriptions a–g on page 133. Press each button step by step on each of the seven pages to construct the figures. When each construction is finished, match each page with a description in the table. Drag each figure to see if it always remains a rhombus. (*Note:* Since a rhombus can be dragged into the shape of a square, we regard a

| Page | Description (a–g) |
|------|-------------------|
| Rhombus 1 | |
| Rhombus 2 | |
| Rhombus 3 | |
| Rhombus 4 | |
| Rhombus 5 | |
| Rhombus 6 | |
| Rhombus 7 | |

square as a special rhombus.) In the table, cross out the names of any pages that construct quadrilaterals that are not always rhombuses.

**3.** List the descriptions from a–g that you think correctly describe a rhombus.

**4.** State the description from a–g that you personally think best describes a rhombus. Try to defend your choice with good reasons.

**5.** Carefully examine the following descriptions and comment on their suitability.

    **a.** A rhombus is any quadrilateral with equal diagonals.

    **b.** A rhombus is any quadrilateral with all sides equal, opposite sides parallel and perpendicular, and bisecting diagonals.

    **c.** A rhombus is any quadrilateral that looks like a rhombus.

    **d.** A rhombus is any quadrilateral with all sides, but not all angles, equal.

**CHALLENGE** Using only logical deduction, can you prove that all of the five properties of a rhombus listed at the beginning and not included in your descriptions in Question 2 can be derived from them? Start from the description as your given assumption and then prove as theorems that a rhombus has each of the other properties listed at the beginning. Apart from using your description as an assumption in these proofs, you can use any new theorems that you prove in the subsequent proofs of the other properties.

# PROVING RHOMBUS PROPERTIES FROM DEFINITIONS

> *When we look at the history of mathematics, we see a kind of lifelike, elemental rhythm. There are periods of exuberant untidy growth, when exciting, vital structures rise upon untried assumptions, and loose ends lie about all over the place. Logic and precision are not unduly honored; because restlessness, enthusiasm, daring and ability to tolerate a measure of confusion are the appropriate qualities of mind at these times. Such periods are followed by pauses for consolidation, when the analysts and systematizers get to work; material is logically ordered, gaps are filled, loose ends are neatly tied up, and rigorous proofs are supplied. Solemn commentators sit in judgment upon great innovators. Whole areas of mathematics are formed into deductive systems, based on sets of unproved, explicitly stated axioms.*
>
> *—L. W. H. Hull, 1969*

We will concern ourselves here with the second part of the quotation above, namely, a logical organization of the properties of a rhombus. The function or purpose of proof here will therefore not be the explanation, discovery, or verification of the properties of a rhombus, but their systematization.

In the preceding part of this activity, you found that each of the following descriptions could be used to accurately construct a rhombus:

**A.** A rhombus is any quadrilateral with two perpendicular axes of symmetry (each through a pair of opposite angles).

**B.** A rhombus is any quadrilateral with perpendicular, bisecting diagonals.

**C.** A rhombus is any quadrilateral with all sides equal.

**D.** A rhombus is any quadrilateral with one pair of adjacent sides equal and opposite sides parallel.

In mathematics, we call such descriptions *definitions*. As we can see, there may be many different, alternative ways in which we can define mathematical objects. We now have to show that all the other properties of a rhombus logically follow as theorems from each of these definitions. We will now give an example for definition B.

*Definition:* A rhombus is any quadrilateral with perpendicular, bisecting diagonals.

Consider the figure where a quadrilateral is given, with diagonals *AC* and *BD* perpendicularly bisecting each other at *O*.

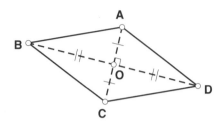

*Theorem 1:* All sides of a rhombus are equal.

**6.** What can you say about triangles *ABO* and *ADO*? Why?

**7.** From Question 6, what can you conclude about sides *AB* and *AD*?

**8.** What can you say about triangles *ABO* and *CBO*? Why?

**9.** From Question 8, what can you conclude about sides *AB*, *CB*, and *AD*?

**10.** What can you say about triangles *ADO* and *CDO*? Why?

**11.** From Question 10, what can you now conclude about all four sides *AD*, *CD*, *AB*, and *CB*?

*Theorem 2:* The diagonals of a rhombus bisect the pairs of opposite angles.

**12.** What can you say about triangles *ABC* and *ADC*? Why?

**13.** From Question 12, what can you conclude about angles *BAC* and *DAC*, as well as angles *BCA* and *DCA*?

**14.** What can you say about triangles *ABD* and *CBD*? Why?

**15.** From Question 14, what can you conclude about angles *ABD* and *CBD*, as well as angles *ADB* and *CDB*?

*Theorem 3:* The diagonals of a rhombus are axes of symmetry.

**16.** From Question 12 in the previous proof, what can you conclude about line *AC*? Why?

**17.** From Question 14 in the previous proof, what can you conclude about line *BD*? Why?

*Theorem 4:* The opposite sides of a rhombus are parallel.

**18.** What can you say about triangles *ABO* and *CDO*? Why?

**19.** From Question 18, what can you conclude about angle *BAO* and angle *DCO*?

**20.** From Question 19, what can you now conclude about sides *AB* and *CD*?

**21.** Use the same argument as in Questions 18–20 to complete the proof for the remaining two sides.

© 2003 Key Curriculum Press

## Present Your Proofs

Write out your proofs clearly for presentation to your group or class.

## Further Exploration

**1.** Now choose any two of the other three possible definitions A, C, and D for a rhombus. For each, show, as in the example on the previous page, how the remaining properties listed at the beginning and not included in your definition can be proved as theorems.

**2.** A concept can also be defined in terms of its relationships with other concepts. A rhombus can also be viewed as a special parallelogram or a special kite, since both of these can be dragged into the shape of a rhombus. Try to define a rhombus by making use of these relationships.

**3.** A rhombus can also be viewed as a special circum quadrilateral (that is, a quadrilateral circumscribed around a circle). Try to define a rhombus as a circum quadrilateral with additional properties.

## Class Discussion

A definition can be seen as an agreement among interested parties about what a specific object is. Although you have now seen that it is possible to define a rhombus in many different ways, it can be very confusing if everyone is using a different definition. It is therefore now necessary to choose a common definition that will be acceptable for the whole class. Have a class discussion to decide which definition of a rhombus is most convenient for you.

In the Isosceles Trapezoid and Cyclic Quadrilateral activities, you should have discovered that an isosceles trapezoid has, among others, the following properties:

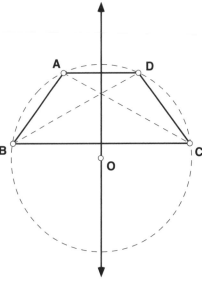

- It has two (distinct) pairs of equal adjacent angles.

- It has at least one pair of equal opposite sides.

- It has at least one axis of symmetry that bisects a pair of opposite sides.

- Its diagonals are equal.

- It has at least one pair of parallel sides.

- It is cyclic.

## DESCRIBE

How would you describe what an isosceles trapezoid is, over the telephone, to someone who is not yet acquainted with an isosceles trapezoid?

1. Which of the following descriptions do you think you would be able to use? Circle these descriptions.

   **a.** An isosceles trapezoid is any quadrilateral with equal diagonals.

   **b.** An isosceles trapezoid is any quadrilateral with at least one axis of symmetry through a pair of opposite sides and one pair of adjacent angles equal.

   **c.** An isosceles trapezoid is any quadrilateral with at least one pair of parallel sides and at least one pair of opposite sides equal.

   **d.** An isosceles trapezoid is any cyclic quadrilateral with at least one pair of opposite sides parallel.

2. If one or more of the above descriptions are not acceptable in your view, how could you correct or improve them?

One way of testing a description is to construct a figure complying with the description to see if it really gives the desired figure.

**3.** Open the sketch **Iso Trap.gsp** to check each of the descriptions a–d. Press each button step by step to construct the figure. When the construction is finished, drag the figure to see if it always remains an isosceles trapezoid. Also take measurements if necessary.

Match each page of the sketch with a description in the table. Two of the five given constructions are based on the same description, but one of those improves on that description. *Note:* Since an isosceles trapezoid can be dragged into the shape of a rectangle (and a square), we regard rectangles (and

| Page | Description (a–d) |
|------|-------------------|
| Iso Trap 1 | |
| Iso Trap 2 | |
| Iso Trap 3 | |
| Iso Trap 4 | |
| Iso Trap 5 | |

squares) as special isosceles trapezoids. In the table, cross out the names of any pages that construct figures that are not always isosceles trapezoids.

**4.** Which construction improves on one of the descriptions a–d? Write the improved description below.

**5.** One of the descriptions a–d has more information than was actually used in the construction. Which one is it? Rewrite that description here, using only the properties used in the construction.

**6.** Carefully examine the following descriptions and comment on their suitability.

**a.** An isosceles trapezoid is any quadrilateral with perpendicular diagonals.

**b.** An isosceles trapezoid is any quadrilateral that looks like an isosceles trapezoid.

**c.** An isosceles trapezoid is any quadrilateral that has adjacent angles equal.

**d.** An isosceles trapezoid is any quadrilateral with one pair of equal opposite sides, one axis of symmetry that bisects a pair of opposite sides, equal diagonals, and one pair of parallel sides.

**e.** An isosceles trapezoid is any quadrilateral with one axis of symmetry, but not all angles equal.

CHALLENGE    Using only logical deduction, can you prove that all the other properties of an isosceles trapezoid listed at the beginning and not included in the correct descriptions in Questions 3–5 can be derived from them? Start by using one of these descriptions as your given assumption, then prove as theorems that an isosceles trapezoid has each of the other remaining properties listed at the beginning. Apart from using your description as an assumption in these proofs, you can use any new theorems that you prove in the subsequent proofs of the other properties.

## PROVING ISOSCELES TRAPEZOID PROPERTIES FROM DEFINITIONS

In earlier activities, we have seen that proof can have the following functions in mathematics:

*explanation* (providing insight into why something is true)

*discovery* (assisting in the discovery or invention of new results)

*verification* (checking the validity or truth of a statement)

In this activity, however, proof will be used in a completely different way. Here we will focus on organizing the properties of an isosceles trapezoid into a logical system consisting of a definition (an unproved statement) and theorems (proved statements). The purpose is not to verify that these properties are true (we already know from earlier investigations that they are true), but to investigate and compare different possible logical organizations. In this sense, proof is now being used as a means of *systematization* (that is, as a tool to logically organize previously unrelated properties or statements into a deductive system).

A common, but false, conception is that there is only one (correct) definition for each defined object in mathematics; in fact, as we have seen here, several different (correct) definitions may exist. Another misconception is that mathematics always starts with definitions—indeed, no definitions of mathematical objects are present *a priori* in nature. In most cases, mathematics *starts* with problems and only *ends* in definitions and deductive systems.

Here are three examples of different correct, economical definitions for an isosceles trapezoid, which you may have discovered in the preceding section of this activity:

**A.** An isosceles trapezoid is any quadrilateral with at least one pair of parallel sides and equal diagonals.

**B.** An isosceles trapezoid is any quadrilateral with at least one axis of symmetry through a pair of opposite sides.

**C.** An isosceles trapezoid is any cyclic quadrilateral with at least one pair of opposite sides parallel.

Other definitions are also possible. Which is the best? That's a matter of opinion. But, interestingly, whichever you choose as your (unproven) definition, the properties in the other definitions can be proven as theorems. And all the other properties of isosceles trapezoids given at the beginning of this activity can be proven starting from any one of the three definitions.

To illustrate this idea, you'll start with definition C, which is probably least familiar to you as a definition, and answer questions that form the proofs of the other properties of an isosceles trapezoid. We shall restrict ourselves here to the convex cyclic case, but similar proofs can be constructed for the crossed cyclic case.

*Definition:* An isosceles trapezoid is any cyclic quadrilateral with at least one pair of opposite sides parallel.

*Theorem 1:* An isosceles trapezoid has two (distinct) pairs of adjacent equal angles.

Consider the figure, where it is given that *ABCD* is cyclic and $\overline{AD} \parallel \overline{BC}$.

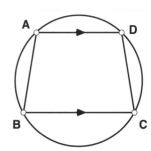

**7.** What is the relationship between angles *A* and *C*? Why?

**8.** What is the relationship between angles *A* and *B*? Why?

**9.** From Questions 7 and 8, what can you now conclude about angle *B* and angle *C*?

**10.** Complete the rest of the proof by showing that angle *A* = angle *D*.

*Theorem 2:* An isosceles trapezoid has at least one pair of opposite sides equal.

Consider the figure, where the givens are as before. Construct $\overline{DE} \parallel \overline{AB}$ as shown.

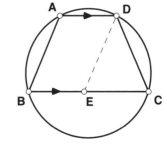

**11.** What can you say about angle *DEC* and angle *ABE*? Why?

**12.** From Theorem 1 above, what can you say about angles *ABE* and *DCE*?

**13.** From Questions 11 and 12, what can you now conclude about angles *DEC* and *DCE*?

**14.** From Question 13, what can you now conclude about triangle *DEC* and its sides *DC* and *DE*?

**15.** What type of quadrilateral is *ABED*? Why?

**16.** From Question 15, what can you say about sides *DE* and *AB*?

**17.** From Questions 14 and 16, what can you now conclude about sides *AB* and *DC*?

*Theorem 3:* An isosceles trapezoid has equal diagonals.

Consider the figure.

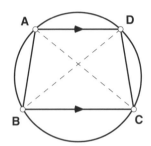

**18.** What can you say about the relationship between triangles *ABC* and *DCB*? Why?

**19.** From Question 18, what can you now conclude about corresponding sides *AC* and *DB*?

*Theorem 4:* An isosceles trapezoid has at least one axis of symmetry through a pair of opposite sides.

Consider the figure. Construct the perpendicular bisector of $\overline{AD}$ at *E* as shown and label its intersection with $\overline{BC}$ as *F*. We now have to prove that this line is an axis of symmetry of *ABCD*; that is, we need to show that $\overleftrightarrow{EF}$ is also the perpendicular bisector of $\overline{BC}$.

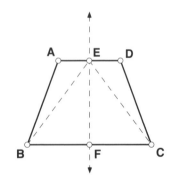

**20.** What can you say about angle *BFE*? Why?

**21.** What can you say about the relationship between triangles *ABE* and *DCE*? Why?

**22.** From Question 21, what can you now conclude about corresponding sides *BE* and *CE*?

**23.** What can you now say about the relationship between triangles *EBF* and *ECF*? Why?

**24.** From Question 23, what can you now conclude about corresponding sides *BF* and *CF*?

**25.** From Question 24, what can you now conclude about line *EF*? Why?

## Systematize More

Now choose either of the definitions A or B for an isosceles trapezoid and show, as in the example, how the other properties listed at the beginning and not included in your definition can be proved as theorems.

## Explore Further Definitions

Investigate, using Sketchpad if necessary, whether each of the following is a correct definition of an isosceles trapezoid. If so, provide a complete deductive systematization of the properties of an isosceles trapezoid, similar to those on the previous page.

**1.** An isosceles trapezoid is any cyclic quadrilateral with at least one pair of opposite sides equal.

**2.** An isosceles trapezoid is any cyclic quadrilateral with at least one pair of adjacent angles equal.

**3.** An isosceles trapezoid is any quadrilateral with at least one pair of opposite sides equal and at least one pair of adjacent angles equal.

**4.** An isosceles trapezoid is any quadrilateral with at least one pair of parallel sides and at least one pair of adjacent angles equal.

5. An isosceles trapezoid is any quadrilateral with two (distinct) pairs of adjacent angles equal.

6. An isosceles trapezoid is any quadrilateral with equal diagonals and at least one pair of opposite sides equal.

Can you formulate some more possible definitions of your own?

## Class Discussion

A definition can be seen as an agreement among interested parties about what a specific object is. Although you have now seen that it is possible to define an isosceles trapezoid in many different ways, it can be very confusing if everyone is using a different definition. It is therefore now necessary to choose a common definition that will be acceptable for the whole class. Have a class discussion to decide which definition of an isosceles trapezoid is most convenient for you.

## Defining and Investigating New Concepts

New mathematical objects are often defined by modifying or extending the definitions or properties of known objects in mathematics. The following are possible examples in relation to the concept of an isosceles trapezoid.

1. Investigate whether a *trilateral trapezoid,* that is, an isosceles trapezoid with at least three equal sides as shown, has any interesting properties in addition to those of an isosceles trapezoid. (*Hint:* Look at how the diagonals divide the angles.) Prove your observations.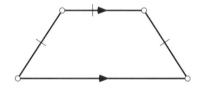

2. Investigate the properties of an *isosceles hexagon,* that is, a hexagon with at least one axis of symmetry through a pair of opposite sides. Prove your observations. Can you generalize further?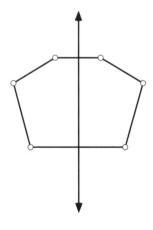

# Teacher Notes

## DISTANCES IN AN EQUILATERAL TRIANGLE
(PAGE 23)

This activity is intended as a first introduction to proof as a means of explanation. The language you use is crucial in this introductory phase of the study of proof. Students find it much more meaningful if instead of saying, as usual, "We cannot be sure that this result is true for all possible variations, and we therefore have to (deductively) prove it to make absolutely sure," you say, "We now know this result to be true from our extensive experimental investigation. Let us now see if we can *explain why* it is true in terms of other well-known geometric results—in other words, how it is the logical consequence of other results."

Avoid using the word *proof* initially; use the word *explanation* instead to emphasize the intended function of the given deductive argument. The word *proof,* in everyday language, predominantly carries with it the idea of verification or conviction (which students grasp firmly once they've explored a result extensively on Sketchpad), and to use it in an introductory context would implicitly convey this meaning, even if the intended meaning was that of explanation.

The verification meaning of proof is, of course, important and will be developed in some of the later activities; at that time, it will become appropriate to start using the word *proof* for the given deductive arguments.

**Prerequisites:** Area formulas for triangles, elementary algebra (factorization).

**Sketch: Distances.gsp.** Additional sketches are **Rhombus Distance.gsp** and **Para Distance.gsp.**

## CONJECTURE

A ready-made sketch is provided, since it is time-consuming for students to first construct an equilateral triangle. In addition, the actual construction of the sketch plays no part in the specific learning objective of making and explaining a conjecture. Students can, however, drag and measure sides of the triangle to check that it is indeed equilateral.

Students will tend to think first that the optimum position for point *P* is at the center of the equilateral triangle, and

it therefore comes as quite a surprise when they later find that the sum of the distances is actually independent of the position of point *P*.

1. The sum of the distances remains constant.

2. Increasing or decreasing the size of the equilateral triangle increases or decreases the sum. However, for a triangle of any given size, moving point *P* around inside the triangle doesn't change the sum.

3. The sum of the distances is not constant. (However, if we consider distances falling completely outside the triangle as negative, the result still holds—see the answer to Question 11.)

4. In an equilateral triangle, the sum of the distances from a point inside the triangle to its sides is constant.

## EXPLAINING

5. The three sides are all equal, but since their lengths may vary, they are indicated by the same variable, *a*.

6. The areas of the triangles are, respectively: $\frac{1}{2}ah_1$, $\frac{1}{2}ah_2$, and $\frac{1}{2}ah_3$.

7. The sum is $\frac{1}{2}ah_1 + \frac{1}{2}ah_2 + \frac{1}{2}ah_3 = \frac{1}{2}a(h_1 + h_2 + h_3)$.

8. Area of whole triangle = sum of areas of small triangles. Therefore, if we represent the area of the whole triangle by *A*, it follows that $h_1 + h_2 + h_3 = \frac{2A}{a}$.

9. For an equilateral triangle of fixed size, its area *A* and its side length *a* are constant. Therefore, the sum of the distances $h_1 + h_2 + h_3$ is also constant.

10. The sum of the distances is equal to the altitude of the original triangle, say *H*. This can be explained as follows:
$$\frac{1}{2}aH = \frac{1}{2}a(h_1 + h_2 + h_3) \longleftrightarrow H = h_1 + h_2 + h_3$$

11. The sum of the distances will remain constant only if there is a common factor $\frac{1}{2}a$ that can be taken out of the three areas; that is, the triangle must be equilateral.

This result is in fact also true if point $P$ is dragged outside the triangle, but an explanation requires the introduction of directed line segments (distances falling completely outside are considered negative). For example, consider the figure below, where point $P$ lies outside as indicated. In this case, the sum of the areas of triangles $PAB$, $PBC$, and $PCA$ is not the area of $\triangle ABC$. To again obtain the area of $\triangle ABC$, we now have to subtract the area of $\triangle PAB$ from the sum of the other two. Therefore, in this case we have $H = h_2 + h_3 - h_1$.

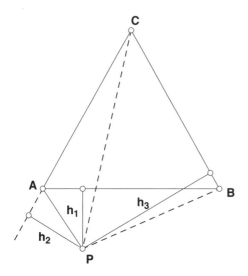

In order to make the general formula $H = h_1 + h_2 + h_3$ work, we therefore need to consider distances as negative if they fall completely outside the triangle. However, considering $P$ outside the triangle may complicate things unnecessarily for students at this stage. You can come back to this result at a later stage to deal with this aspect of it if you wish.

## Further Exploration

1. To find the minimum sum for an arbitrary triangle, the point $P$ has to be situated at the vertex opposite the longest side (where the altitude is the smallest).

2. a. The sum of the distances from $P$ to the sides of a rhombus is constant (see the following sketches). See the example sketch **Rhombus Distance.gsp.**

Distance P to j = 3.36 cm
Distance P to k = 1.74 cm
Distance P to m = 0.81 cm
Distance P to n = 2.43 cm
Distance P to j + Distance P to k
$\qquad + \ldots + \ldots = 8.33$ cm

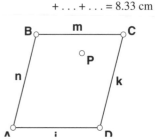

Distance P to j = 2.02 cm
Distance P to k = 1.52 cm
Distance P to m = 2.15 cm
Distance P to n = 2.64 cm
Distance P to j + Distance P to k
$\qquad + \ldots + \ldots = 8.33$ cm

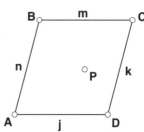

  b. The proof is the same as that for the equilateral triangle, since all the sides are equal. The result is generalizable to *equisided* polygons. In general, we would have for any equisided $n$-gon $A_n$ $(n > 2)$ with side length $a$ that $\sum_{i=1}^{n} h_i = 2\left(\frac{A_n}{a}\right)$.

3. a. The sum of the distances from $P$ to the sides of a parallelogram is constant (see below). See the example sketch **Para Distance.gsp.**

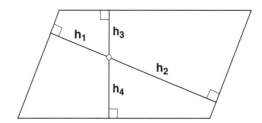

b. The sum $h_1 + h_2$ is constant, since the distance between the two opposite parallel sides is constant. Similarly, $h_3 + h_4$ is constant. Therefore, $h_1 + h_2 + h_3 + h_4$ is constant (equal to the sum of the two distances between the pairs of opposite sides). The result is generalizable to any polygon with an even number of sides and opposite sides parallel but not necessarily equal (that is, a *parallel-2n*-gon ($n > 1$)), where the sum of the $2n$ distances to the sides will be equal to the sum of the $n$ distances between the pairs of opposite sides.

Another possibility to consider is the generalization to three dimensions (and more). Since the 3D analog of a triangle is a tetrahedron, students may first want to consider a regular tetrahedron. Instead of working with areas and distances, they will now need to work with volumes and areas. After further reflection, they should realize that the sum of the distances to the four faces of a tetrahedron, with all four faces having the same area $a$, would also be constant. For example, a point $P$ inside the tetrahedron divides it into four tetrahedra, so that

$$\frac{1}{3}aH = \frac{1}{3}a(h_1 + h_2 + h_3 + h_4) \longleftrightarrow H = h_1 + h_2 + h_3 + h_4$$

Note that if the area of each face is the same, the height $H$ from each face to the opposite vertex must also be the same, since its volume is constant. But this does not imply that the tetrahedron is necessarily regular.

4. The sum of the distances to the sides of an equi-angled pentagon is also constant. The result can be generalized to any equi-angled polygon (see Sharygin 2000, 50).

5. Some of the main assumptions are:

- The three beaches are perfectly straight.

- The island is perfectly equilateral.

- There are no other natural obstacles such as rivers, swamps, or dangerous animals that the surfer may want to avoid.

- The space between the beaches is flat everywhere (that is, there are no hills or valleys).

- The three beaches are equally good for surfing (which is why she visits each with equal frequency).

# WATER SUPPLY I: FOUR TOWNS (PAGE 27)

The two activities Water Supply I: Four Towns and Water Supply II: Three Towns are real-world problems structured to introduce students to these concepts: the perpendicular bisector, the circumcenter, the theorem involving the concurrency of the perpendicular bisectors of any triangle, and the explanation (proof) of that theorem. Although the activities could be done independently of one another, it is not recommended. Students are given a quadrilateral problem first so they can discover that the perpendicular bisectors of a polygon are not necessarily always concurrent, and we hope they will experience some surprise in the second Water Supply activity when they find that for a triangle the perpendicular bisectors are always concurrent.

**Prerequisites:** None.

**Sketches: Water Supply I.gsp** and **Water Supply II.gsp.** Additional sketch is **Water Supply Ib.gsp.**

## INVESTIGATE

Answers to Questions 1 and 2 will vary. Students are expected to first measure the distances from point $P$ to the four vertices and then to drag point $P$ until all four distances are equal. You might point out to your students that this is essentially the *guess-and-check* problem-solving strategy.

## A SIMPLER PROBLEM

This part of the activity is intended to develop the idea that the perpendicular bisector is the set of points equidistant from the endpoints of a line segment.

3. Students should notice the following:

   a. Any point on the traced path is equidistant from the two vertices.

   b. The traced path is perpendicular to the line segment connecting the two vertices.

   c. The traced path bisects the line segment connecting the two vertices.

4. When the vertices are in their original places, the four perpendicular bisectors of the sides of the quadrilateral are concurrent.

## A More General Problem

5. Answers will vary. At this stage, students may believe that the perpendicular bisectors of any quadrilateral are concurrent. In Question 6, the students will discover that they're not.

6. The perpendicular bisectors of the sides of a quadrilateral are not necessarily concurrent.

7. Answers will vary.

8. Since all the towns are equidistant from point $P$, they must lie on a circle centered at $P$.

## Further Exploration

1. Construct a circle and any four points on its circumference. These four points are all equidistant from the center, since the circle has constant radius.

2. Some of the main assumptions are

   • The four villages all lie on the same plane.

   • The space between the villages is flat everywhere (that is, there are no hills or valleys).

   • There are no other natural obstacles such as rivers, swamps, or dangerous animals that people may want to avoid.

   • The villages are all the same size (because if they were not, it might be much better to place the reservoir closer to the largest village).

3. First, it seems reasonable to conjecture that the "best" point ought to be located somewhere in the feasible region formed by the four respective circumcenters $E$, $F$, $G$, and $H$ of the four triangles $ABC$, $BCD$, $CDA$, and $BAD$. Second, since we want to attempt to minimize the differences between all the distances, we need to minimize the sum of the absolute values of the differences to obtain the "best" point, for example,

$$|PA - PB| + |PA - PC| + |PA - PD| +$$
$$|PB - PC| + |PB - PD| + |PC - PD|$$

PA = 5.67 cm
PB = 5.29 cm
PC = 5.68 cm
PD = 4.64 cm

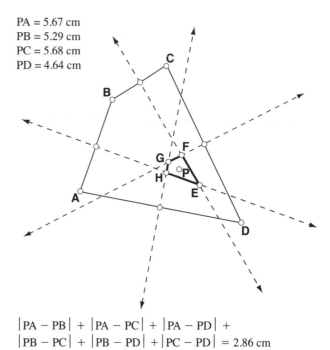

$$|PA - PB| + |PA - PC| + |PA - PD| +$$
$$|PB - PC| + |PB - PD| + |PC - PD| = 2.86 \text{ cm}$$

An example sketch is given in **Water Supply Ib.gsp** where the "best" position can be obtained by dragging $P$ until the desired minimum is obtained.

4. To solve this problem, students first have to realize that buildings farther away appear smaller. Therefore to make a visual comparison between the respective heights of any two buildings, they need to be equidistant from both buildings. The required positions can therefore be obtained by constructing the perpendicular bisectors of the sides $AB$, $BC$, and $CD$ and finding the respective intersections with the route.

# WATER SUPPLY II: THREE TOWNS (PAGE 31)

In this activity, students investigate a real-world problem and discover that the perpendicular bisectors of the sides of a triangle are concurrent. Although this activity could be done independently, it is intended to follow Water Supply I: Four Towns. In that activity, students investigate a case (a quadrilateral) in which the perpendicular bisectors are *not* concurrent. Seeing that case first should make it seem more significant to students that perpendicular bisectors are concurrent in a triangle.

## INVESTIGATE

1–2. Answers will vary.

## A More General Problem

3. Students should observe and conjecture that the perpendicular bisectors of any triangle are always concurrent, although in a quadrilateral they are not. Make sure that they explore a large variety of different triangles to convince themselves of the generality of this result.

4. Students should find as they drag the vertices that the sketch supports the conjecture they made in Question 3.

## EXPLAINING

First give students an opportunity to try to explain the result on their own before giving them the Explaining section of the activity.

5. All the points are equidistant from village 1 and village 2.

6. All the points are equidistant from village 2 and village 3.

7. Point *P* is equidistant from village 1 and village 3 and must therefore lie on the perpendicular bisector of the line segment connecting village 1 to village 3.

8. The perpendicular bisector of the third side must also pass through point *P*.

*Note:* The concurrency of the perpendicular bisectors and the existence of a circumcircle are traditionally proved (explained) by means of congruency as follows. Students may gain insights by comparing this proof with the one based on equidistance in the activity.

## Proof

Consider the triangle *ABC* shown here. Construct the perpendicular bisectors of $\overline{AB}$ and $\overline{AC}$ to intersect in *F*. Join *F* to *G*, the midpoint of $\overline{BC}$. It is now necessary to prove that $m\angle FGB = 90°$—in other words, that $\overline{FG}$ is also the perpendicular bisector of $\overline{BC}$.

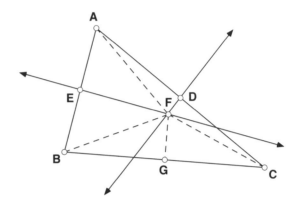

$\triangle AEF$ is congruent to $\triangle BEF$ (SAS); therefore, $FB = FA$. $\triangle ADF$ is congruent to $\triangle CDF$ (SAS); therefore, $FC = FA$. Thus, $FB = FC$, and it follows that triangles *BGF* and *CGF* are also congruent (SSS). Therefore, $m\angle FGB = m\angle FGC = 90°$.

## Further Exploration

1. The circumcenter falls inside if the triangle is acute, on the hypotenuse if it is a right triangle, and outside if it is obtuse.

2. a. The circle now passes through all four vertices.

   b. The fourth perpendicular bisector also passes through the intersection of the other three.

   c. Students should note that if three of the perpendicular bisectors of a quadrilateral are concurrent, the fourth perpendicular bisector is concurrent with the other three and the quadrilateral is cyclic (its four vertices all lie on a circle).

The proof of the result in Further Exploration, Question 2c, is similar to the one for the triangle. In quadrilateral *ABCD*, consider the perpendicular bisectors of sides *AB*, *BC*, and *CD*, and assume that they are concurrent in point *P*.

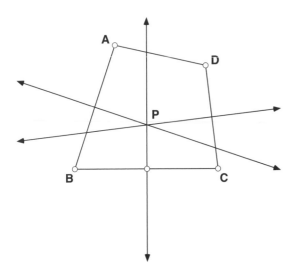

All the points on the perpendicular bisector of $\overline{AB}$ are equidistant from points $A$ and $B$. Similarly, all the points on the perpendicular bisector of $\overline{BC}$ are equidistant from points $B$ and $C$. Also, all the points on the perpendicular bisector of $\overline{CD}$ are equidistant from points $C$ and $D$. Therefore, if all the perpendicular bisectors are concurrent in the same point $P$, point $P$ must be equidistant from points $A$, $B$, $C$, and $D$. It follows that a circle can be drawn, with point $P$ as its center, passing through all four vertices. Since point $P$ is equidistant from points $A$ and $D$, it must therefore also lie on the perpendicular bisector of $\overline{AD}$.

Similarly, if four perpendicular bisectors of a pentagon are concurrent, the fifth perpendicular bisector is always concurrent with the intersection of the other four, and the pentagon is cyclic. This is now easily generalized to the following: If $n - 1$ perpendicular bisectors of an $n$-gon are concurrent, all of them are (and therefore the $n$-gon is cyclic).

## TRIANGLE ANGLE SUM (PAGE 34)

It is still advisable to avoid using the word *proof* and to focus on the explanation of the result rather than on its verification. It should again be emphasized to students that no amount of experimentation provides us with an adequate explanation; for that, we require some form of logical explanation.

It is important not to delay the introduction to logical explanation (proof) too long, because a prolonged purely empirical approach can become so fossilized in students' thinking that it is difficult to change later. Many students do exhibit a need for deeper understanding, and the sooner this habit of mind is cultivated the better.

Although you could let students discover the angle sum result of a triangle simply by measuring each angle and adding them with a calculator, such an approach, according to the van Hiele theory, does not provide an appropriate conceptual structure for the proof (explanation) that is to follow later. The initial empirical activity given here, however, provides the conceptual and visual framework on which the formal explanation (proof) is later built.

**Prerequisites:** Properties of parallel lines.

**Sketch: Triangle Sum.gsp.**

## CONJECTURE

1. Because of the translations and rotations (and therefore the corresponding congruence of angles), the three angles of the triangle form a straight line. In other words, the sum of the angles of a triangle is always equal to the measure of a straight angle. Students should look at specific triangles as well as limiting cases.

2. The sum of the measures of the angles of a triangle is 180°.

## EXPLAINING

3. $m\angle BAC = m\angle ECD$ (corresponding angles).

4. $m\angle ABC = m\angle BCE$ (alternate angles).

5. $m\angle ACB + m\angle BCE + m\angle ECD = 180°$. ($ACD$ is a straight line from construction.)

6. Therefore $m\angle ACB + m\angle ABC + m\angle BAC = 180°$.

7. When a transversal cuts across two parallel lines, corresponding and alternate angles formed are equal. The measure of a straight angle is 180°.

## Present Your Explanation

Here, you could discuss different forms of presentation for logical arguments. For example, compare an essay-type with a traditional two-column-type presentation of a logical argument. Students should have some freedom of choice, provided that their presentations are systematic and logical.

## Further Exploration

1. a. $m\angle DBA = m\angle BAC$ (alternate angles). $m\angle EBC = m\angle BCA$ (alternate angles). But $m\angle DBA + m\angle ABC + m\angle CBE = 180°$. ($DBE$ is a straight line from construction.) Therefore, $m\angle ACB + m\angle ABC + m\angle BAC = 180°$.

   b. There is hardly any difference between the two explanations, except that the first uses alternate angles and corresponding angles, whereas the second uses only alternate angles. The first explanation also requires the construction of two lines (or rays), whereas the second requires only one line. It could therefore be argued that the second explanation is (slightly) more economical than the first.

## QUADRILATERAL ANGLE SUM (PAGE 37)

**Prerequisites:** Students should be familiar with the sum of the measures of the angles of a triangle. Even better, they have completed the previous activity Triangle Angle Sum. It will also help if they know that the sum of the measures of the exterior angles of a simple closed polygon is 360°. This activity also works well as preparation for the next activity, Crossed Quadrilateral Sum.

**Sketch: Quad Sum.gsp.**

## CONJECTURE

1. All four quadrilaterals, $ABCD$, $HCBI$, $FEDC$, and $CHGF$, are congruent to each other.

2. There are no overlaps or gaps between the angles. Since these angles fit around a point, their sum must be 360°.

3. The same observation holds for any convex or concave quadrilateral.

4. a. $m\angle ADC = m\angle FCD$ because a half-turn around the midpoint of $\overline{DC}$ maps these two angles onto each other.

   b. $m\angle BAD = m\angle HCF$ because a translation of quadrilateral $ABCD$ to $CHGF$ maps these two angles onto each other. Also, students could describe the two rotations in the sketch that map $ABCD$ to $CHGF$.

   c. $m\angle CBA = m\angle LBCH$ because a half-turn around the midpoint of $\overline{BC}$ maps these two angles onto each other.

5. Since the measure of each of the interior angles of $ABCD$ equals the measure of one of the four angles around vertex $C$, it follows that the sum of the measures of the angles of any convex or concave quadrilateral must also be 360°. (Students could also tessellate the quadrilateral around the other vertices.)

6. Students should notice that in the concave case the angles still fit around the same vertex without any overlaps or gaps between them; therefore, the result is also true for concave quadrilaterals.

**CHALLENGE** Here, students are given the opportunity to attempt their own logical explanations.

## EXPLAINING

7. Any convex or concave quadrilateral can be divided into two triangles by drawing an *interior* diagonal. Since the sum of the measures of the angles of any triangle is 180°, the sum of the angles of any convex or concave quad is $2 \times 180° = 360°$.

8. Consider the convex and concave quadrilaterals *ABCD* shown below. In both cases, the sum of the measures of the exterior angles is 360°. Therefore, $m\angle p + m\angle q + m\angle r + m\angle s = 360°$, and the sum of the measures of the interior angles is therefore given by

$$(180° - m\angle p) + (180° - m\angle q)$$
$$+ (180° - m\angle r) + (180° - m\angle s)$$

$$= 720° - (m\angle p + m\angle q + m\angle r + m\angle s)$$

$$= 720° - 360° = 360°$$

Note that in the concave case shown, the measure of angle *p* is negative in relation to the other angles, since it has an opposite direction of rotation. The measure of the interior angle at *B* (the reflex angle) is therefore

$$180° - m\angle p = 180° + \left| m\angle p \right|$$

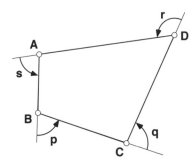

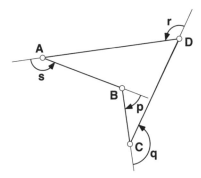

## Present Your Explanation

Here, students are given the opportunity to summarize and present their arguments for discussion.

### Further Exploration

One way to arrive at a general formula is to observe that any concave or convex *n*-gon (for $n > 2$) can be divided into $n - 2$ triangles, and therefore the sum of the measure of the interior angles is $(n - 2)180°$.

Another way is to use the fact that the sum of the measures of the exterior angles of any polygon is 360° (assuming positive orientation). The sum of the measures of the interior angles of any concave or convex *n*-gon (for $n > 2$) is therefore given by

$$(n \times 180°) - \text{sum of exterior angles} = (n \times 180°) - 360°$$
$$= (n - 2)\,180°$$

# CROSSED QUADRILATERAL SUM (PAGE 40)

Sketchpad makes it natural for students to explore shapes that are not traditionally studied. These shapes include concave and crossed polygons. One purpose of this activity is to make students aware of the limitations of the standard angle measurement of Sketchpad and to let them discover that (and explain why) the sum of the measures of the interior angles of a crossed quadrilateral is 720°.

For a concave quadrilateral, the measures of the four interior angles actually do not sum to 360° in Sketchpad. The reason for this is that Sketchpad does not measure angles greater than 180°. As the activity demonstrates, this can be rectified by measuring the corresponding arc lengths.

This activity begins with a lot of reading that might be most efficiently presented to students as a whole-class demonstration as follows:

$m\angle DAB = 70.4°$
$m\angle ABC = 96.1°$
$m\angle BCD = 122.2°$
$m\angle CDA = 71.4°$
$m\angle DAB + m\angle ABC + m\angle BCD \ m\angle CDA = 360°$

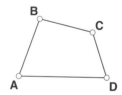

$m\angle DAB = 13.2°$
$m\angle ABC = 123.9°$
$m\angle BCD = 39.4°$
$m\angle CDA = 71.4°$
$m\angle DAB + m\angle ABC + m\angle BCD + m\angle CDA = 247.9°$

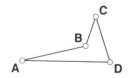

$m\angle DAB = 13.2°$
$m\angle ABC = 123.9°$
$m\angle BCD = 39.4°$
$m\angle CDA = 71.4°$
$m\angle DAB + m\angle ABC + m\angle BCD + m\angle CDA = 247.9°$

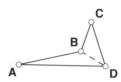

Construct a convex quadrilateral. Measure the angles and sum them. Drag a vertex until the quadrilateral becomes concave. The sum will start to vary at this point. Ask students whether they think this means the quadrilateral angle sum theorem applies only to convex quadrilaterals. Assuming some do reach this erroneous conclusion, draw a diagonal and ask students to recall the explanation from the Quadrilateral Angle Sum activity. Is there any reason the explanation for the quadrilateral angle sum shouldn't apply to this concave quadrilateral? At this point, students should begin to notice that Sketchpad is not measuring the interior angle whose measure is greater than 180° but is instead measuring an angle outside the polygon. Explain that Sketchpad always measures angles less than 180°, but that students will work in a sketch that gets around that limitation by measuring arc angles instead. Then briefly direct students' attention to the figures on the worksheet that illustrate a possible definition of "interior" angles in a crossed quadrilateral. Students will then be prepared to work on their own starting at the Conjecture section of the activity.

**Prerequisites:** Students should be familiar with the sum of the measures of the angles of a convex quadrilateral. It is even better preparation for them to have completed the previous activity, Quadrilateral Angle Sum. It will also help if they know that the sum of the measures of the exterior angles of a simple closed polygon is 360°.

**Sketch: Crossed Quad Sum.gsp.**

## CONJECTURE

1. The sum of the measures of the interior angles of a convex quadrilateral is 360°.

2. The standard angle measures do not sum to 360° for a concave quadrilateral; the sum actually varies.

3. Responses will vary. The diagonal *DB* divides the quadrilateral into two triangles, so the sum of the measures of the interior angles should still be $2 \times 180° = 360°$.

4. Measure of interior angle *CDA* = 360° − standard Sketchpad measure of angle *CDA*.

5. The sum of the arc angle measures gives the correct value for the interior angle sum of both a convex and a concave quadrilateral.

6. Answers will vary. Students might guess that the sum of the measures of the interior angles of a crossed quadrilateral is also 360°.

7. Responses will vary.

8. The sum of the measures of the interior angles of a crossed quadrilateral is 720°, as shown by the arc angle sum.

It should also be pointed out that some students may at first want to argue that crossed quadrilaterals are not quadrilaterals at all. This view corresponds to the technique of *monster-barring* described by Imre Lakatos in his famous book *Proof and Refutations* (1976). This can create a valuable opportunity for some classroom discussion and debate. Essentially, the issue is how one chooses to define the quadrilaterals, or for that matter, polygons in general. However, within a dynamic geometry environment, a simple closed polygon is easily transformed into a crossed polygon, and it therefore seems natural to simply consider the crossed polygons as special cases.

9. Neither. The sum of the measures of the arc angles is now displayed as 1080°. There are now at least three reflexive arc angles, so the arc angle sum has to be more than that in the crossed case. However, since all the arc angles fall outside in this case, they can hardly be considered "interior" angles. The actual sum of the

measures of the "interior" angles can be determined from the arc angles as follows:

$$(360° - m\angle A) + (360° - m\angle B) +$$
$$\quad (360° - m\angle C) + (360° - m\angle D) = 1080° \longrightarrow$$

$$m\angle A + m\angle B + m\angle C + m\angle D$$
$$\quad = 4 \times 360° - 1080° = 360°$$

The sum of the simple angle measures will be correct only if the "inside out" quadrilateral is convex. If it is concave, we have the same problem as before: Sketchpad does not display the measurement of the one reflex angle correctly, so the angles do not sum to 360°.

## EXPLAINING

10. measure of reflexive $\angle ADC$ = 360° − measure acute $\angle ADC$ and measure of reflexive $\angle BAD$ = 360° − measure acute $\angle BAD$.

11. $m\angle BOD = m$ acute $\angle ADC + m$ acute $\angle BAD$ (exterior angle of $\triangle DOA$).

12. $m\angle BOD = m\angle BCD + m\angle ABC$ (exterior angle of $\triangle BOC$).

13. $m$ acute $\angle ADC + m$ acute $\angle BAD = m\angle BCD + m\angle ABC$.

14. $m$ reflexive $\angle ADC + m$ reflexive $\angle BAD + m\angle BCD + m\angle ABC = (360° - m$ acute $\angle ADC) + (360° - m$ acute $\angle BAD) + (m$ acute $\angle ACD) + (m$ acute $\angle BAD) = 720°$.

## ADDITIONAL NOTES

Some students may have difficulty understanding why two reflexive angles that seem to fall outside a crossed quadrilateral are considered "interior" angles. A more detailed discussion, such as the following, may help.

One way to extend the notion of interior angles to crossed quadrilaterals is by first carefully analyzing and defining the notion of internal angles for convex and concave quadrilaterals and then consistently applying that definition to crossed quadrilaterals. (This is a strategy often used in mathematics to extend certain concepts beyond their original domain(s)—for example, in extending positive integers to negative integers.)

Suppose we walk counterclockwise from *A* to *B*, *B* to *C*, and so on, around the perimeters of the convex and concave quadrilaterals shown in the figure. The internal angle at each vertex can then be defined precisely as the angle through which the *next side* must be rotated *counterclockwise* (with the vertex as rotation center) to coincide with the *preceding side.*

Using exactly this definition, the internal angles of a crossed quadrilateral can now be obtained by walking around its perimeter as shown.

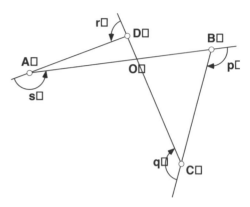

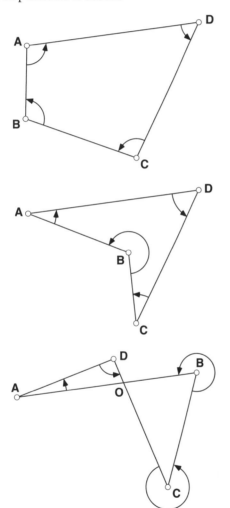

The sum of the measures of the interior angles of a crossed quadrilateral can also be determined from the sum of the measures of the exterior angles (see the figure above). Here the sum of the measures of the turning (exterior) angles is equal to 0°. Imagine yourself as a turtle walking around the perimeter, turning at each vertex. After turning clockwise twice, you then turn counterclockwise twice to arrive back at *A* facing in the same direction as you were at the beginning. Therefore, $m\angle p + m\angle q + m\angle r + m\angle s = 0°$, and the interior angle sum measure is given by

$$(180° - m\angle p) + (180° - m\angle q) +$$
$$(180° - m\angle r) + (180° - m\angle s)$$

$$= 4 \times 180° - (m\angle p + m\angle q + m\angle r + m\angle s)$$

$$= 720° - 0° = 720°$$

The traditional curriculum normally treats the interior angle sums of triangles and quadrilaterals first, before dealing with their exterior angle sums (and then proving them in terms of their interior angle sums). However, from a logical point of view, we could just as easily first deal with the exterior angle sums of polygons, then use them to prove the interior angle sums of polygons.

## Further Exploration

You may also want to further challenge your stronger students to try to find a general formula for the interior angle sum of *any* polygon (including crossed ones). For this purpose, you might give them figures to explore like those shown here.

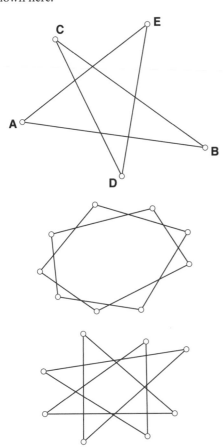

## GENERAL FORMULA

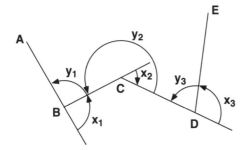

Imagine a turtle walking counterclockwise from *A* to *B* in the diagram shown here, turning through angle $x_1$, moving along segment *BC*, turning through angle $x_2$, and so on, until the figure closes and the turtle is once again facing in

the direction of $\overline{AB}$. The sum of the measures of the turning angles must therefore be a multiple of 360°. Therefore,

$$\sum x_i = k \cdot 360° \dots k = 0; 1; 2; 3; \text{etc.}$$

The sum of the measures of the interior angles is now simply the difference between $n \cdot 180°$ and the sum of the measures of the turning angles, where *n* is the number of vertices. Therefore,

$$S = \sum y_i = n \cdot 180° - \sum x_i = n \cdot 180° - k \cdot 360°$$
$$= 180° (n - 2k)$$

For a simple closed polygon, such as a triangle, a convex or concave quadrilateral, and so on, the total turning is $k = 1$ because we undergo one full rotation walking around its perimeter. Students can use a pen or pencil to rotate one side onto the other, continuing around the perimeter, and note the *total turning* of the pen or pencil until they return to their starting point. For example, for the star pentagon shown, $k = 2$, and for the other two figures it is respectively 2 and 3. Once the *k* value of a polygon has been determined, the interior angle sum can be found by substitution in the formula given above.

# ISOSCELES TRAPEZOID (PAGE 45)

This activity provides students with the opportunity to explore visually (as well as by measurement) the properties of an isosceles trapezoid, and to logically explain these properties in terms of line symmetry. On a conceptual basis, it is therefore intended as an exploratory activity at van Hiele Level 1 (visualization) and van Hiele Level 2 (analysis). Since it is assumed here that students are not yet at van Hiele Level 3 (which involves the logical ordering of the properties of a concept as well as its hierarchical classification), a formal, economical definition of isosceles trapezoids should *not* be given to the students at this stage. It will be dealt with later on.

**Prerequisites:** Knowledge of line (bilateral) symmetry.

**Sketch: Isosceles Trapezoid.gsp.** This sketch is not required.

## CONJECTURE

1. The isosceles trapezoid has one pair of equal opposite sides and one pair of parallel sides.

2. It has two pairs of equal, adjacent angles.

3. The diagonals are equal.

4. All of the above statements apply to the crossed isosceles trapezoid.

5. Sketchpad shows all four angles equal for any crossed isosceles trapezoid. (However, the "interior" angles of a crossed isosceles trapezoid $CDD'C'$ can be defined as shown in the figure. See the activity Crossed Quadrilateral, in which the interior angles of a crossed quad are discussed in more detail.)

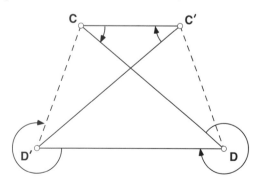

## EXPLAINING

6. All the properties follow directly from the line of symmetry, $\overleftrightarrow{AB}$. $\overline{CD}$ maps onto $\overline{C'D'}$, and therefore one pair of opposite sides are equal. Angles $C$ and $D$ respectively map onto angles $C'$ and $D'$, and therefore two pairs of adjacent angles are equal. $\overline{CC'}$ and $\overline{DD'}$ are both perpendicular to the line of symmetry and are therefore parallel to each other. $\overline{CD'}$, upon reflection over $\overleftrightarrow{AB}$, maps onto $\overline{C'D}$, and therefore the diagonals are equal.

7. From symmetry, it follows that both triangles $OCC'$ and $ODD'$ are isosceles triangles ($\overline{C'O}$ maps to $\overline{CO}$, and so on). But since vertical angles $C'OC$ and $DOD'$ are equal, the corresponding base angles of these two isosceles triangles must be equal.

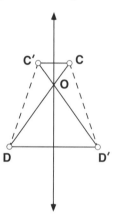

## Further Exploration

1. Students should observe that they can obtain a general rectangle with all angles equal, but not necessarily with all sides equal. The question of whether it is still an isosceles trapezoid is bound to create problems with some students who are at van Hiele Levels 1 and 2 and who might not want to perceive a rectangle as a special case of an isosceles trapezoid. (For example, some might say that a rectangle has all its angles equal, but an isosceles trapezoid does not.) On the other hand, some might say that a rectangle is a special case, since it has all the properties of an isosceles trapezoid discovered in Questions 1–3; it is special simply because it has an additional property (all angles equal).

The first view is called a *partition* view; the second, a *hierarchical* view. It is important that you, as the teacher, do not show a particular bias toward either view, but try to remain neutral in the student discussion. The purpose of this question at this point is merely to stimulate discussion among students, not to lead to a complete resolution. In fact, you should not attempt to fully resolve this issue until the majority of the students have reached at least Van Hiele Level 3 and they have begun the treatment of a formal definition for an isosceles trapezoid (see Chapter 5).

2. Students will observe that they can make all sides equal, thus obtaining a square. A discussion similar to that in Question 1, around a partition view and a hierarchical view, is likely to occur here.

3. This question is intended to assist students in developing a more complete conceptualization of an isosceles trapezoid and its relationship to other quadrilaterals. For example, here they will notice that while an isosceles trapezoid can be dragged into the shape of a rectangle or a square, it cannot be dragged into the shape of a (general) parallelogram, a (general) rhombus, or a (general) kite.

4. The perpendicular bisectors of the sides are concurrent, and therefore the isosceles trapezoid is cyclic (since the point of concurrency is equidistant from all four vertices). This can be logically explained as follows.

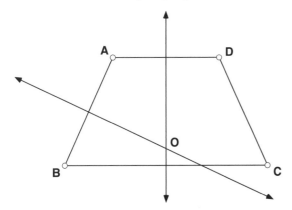

Consider the isosceles trapezoid shown here. From symmetry, it follows that the perpendicular bisectors of both $\overline{AD}$ and $\overline{BC}$ coincide with the axis of symmetry.

The perpendicular bisector of $\overline{AB}$ intersects the axis of symmetry at point $O$. But since $\overline{AB}$ maps onto $\overline{DC}$ around the axis of symmetry, its perpendicular bisector must also map onto the perpendicular bisector of $\overline{DC}$ (and vice versa), implying that these two perpendicular bisectors must intersect each other at point $O$. Since the perpendicular bisectors are concurrent, there exists a point equidistant from all four vertices, and a circle can be drawn with point $O$ as center and $\overline{AO}$ as radius (see the Water Supply activities, earlier on).

# CYCLIC QUADRILATERAL (PAGE 48)

**Prerequisites:** An inscribed angle has half the measure of its intercepted arc.

**Sketch: Cyclic Quad.gsp.**

## CONJECTURE

1. The opposite angles of a (convex) cyclic quad are supplementary.

2. The perpendicular bisectors of the sides of a cyclic quad always remain concurrent.

   Some students may observe that opposite angles are no longer supplementary when the cyclic quad becomes crossed. Note that if we consider directed angles as discussed in the Crossed Quadrilateral Sum activity, the sums of the two pairs of opposite angles in a crossed cyclic quad are both equal to 360° (see figure). Therefore, in general we can say that for *any* cyclic quad, the sums of the two pairs of opposite angles are equal.

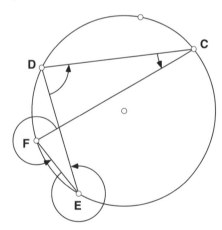

## Further Exploration

We can obtain as special cases a general isosceles trapezoid, a general rectangle, and a square, but not a general parallelogram or a general rhombus. Students might also obtain a certain general kite (when its axis of symmetry passes through the center of a circle), and you might also ask them to investigate and explain its property of having one pair of opposite right angles (angles in a semicircle).

## EXPLAINING

3. The circumcenter is equidistant from all four vertices (radii are equal), but each perpendicular bisector is the locus of all the points equidistant from the endpoints (vertices) of each side. Therefore, each perpendicular bisector must pass through the circumcenter.

   Conversely, you may want to point out that this is a very useful condition for any polygon to be inscribed in a circle (to be cyclic). For example, for any polygon to have a circumcircle, it must have a point that is equidistant from all the vertices. Therefore, the perpendicular bisectors must meet in a single point; that is, they must be concurrent.

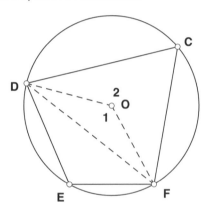

4. Consider the convex cyclic quadrilateral shown above. Central angle $O_1$ and inscribed angle $C$ intercept the same arc, so $m\angle O_1 = 2 \cdot m\angle C$. Likewise, $m\angle O_2 = 2 \cdot m\angle E$. But $m\angle O_1 + m\angle O_2 = 360°$; therefore $2 \cdot m\angle E + 2 \cdot m\angle C = 360°$, which reduces to $m\angle E + m\angle C = 180°$. Similarly, it can be shown that angles $D$ and $F$ are supplementary.

## Further Exploration

1. They are both equal (to 360°).

2. The two sums of the measures of the sets of alternate angles of a cyclic hexagon are equal. (This result is also true for certain types of crossed cyclic hexagons, provided that we work with directed angles, as discussed in the Crossed Quadrilateral Sum activity.)

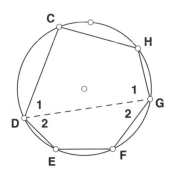

3. Consider the figure shown above. $m\angle C + m\angle G_1 = 180°$, and $m\angle E + m\angle E + m\angle G_2 = 180°$. Therefore, $m\angle C + m\angle E + m\angle G = 360°$. Similarly, it can be shown that the sum of the measures of the other set of alternate angles is also 360°.

4. Angles $A$ and $C$, and angles $B$ and $D$, are the two sets of alternate angles. The two sums of the measures of the sets of alternate angles of a cyclic quadrilateral are equal.

5. In general, for certain types of cyclic $2n$-gons where $n > 1$, the two sums of the measures of the sets of alternate angles are equal. (For convex ones, these sums are equal to $180°(n - 1)$.) The following theorem in this regard is proved in de Villiers (1996, 183–187):

*If $A_1 A_2 \ldots A_{2n}$ ($n > 1$) is any cyclic 2n-gon in which vertex $A_1 \rightarrow y\, A_{1+k}$ (vertex $A_i$ is joined to $A_{i+k}$), the two sums of alternate interior angles are each equal to $m\pi$ (where $m = n - k$ and $k$ is the total turning we would undergo by walking around the perimeter of the polygon).*

# THE CENTER OF GRAVITY OF A TRIANGLE
## (PAGE 51)

This activity introduces students to the idea that even after a result has been found to be true experimentally, creating a logical explanation for the result can be an intellectual challenge similar to the solution of a crossword or other puzzle. Experience with students has shown that they find it far more reasonable to accept that some people (for example, mathematicians) could be motivated by such intellectual challenges and activities than to accept that they would indulge in such an activity simply for the sake of verification.

You could further point out that different people have different interests. For example, not everybody is excited by bungee jumping, mountaineering, marathon running, crossword puzzles, athletics, golf, bowling, cooking, tennis, or any given activity. This does not mean that someone who is not strongly motivated in any of these areas could not have some appreciation and respect for those who have mastered, and found meaning in, a particular discipline. The challenge is therefore to inculcate and encourage some appreciation and understanding of the discipline of mathematics (and in particular of deductive reasoning) in those who do not aspire to become mathematicians or who will not seriously apply mathematics in later life.

**Prerequisites:** Midpoint triangle theorem, properties of parallelograms, triangle area formula.

**Sketches: Triangle Median.gsp** and **Centroid.gsp.** Additional sketches are **Quad Centroid.gsp, Ceva.gsp, Ceva Concurrency.gsp,** and **Ceva Pentagon.gsp.**

## CONJECTURE: LOCATING THE CENTROID

1. Segment $DE$ is parallel to $\overline{AC}$.

2. The midpoint of $\overline{DE}$.

3. Responses will vary.

4. It is a straight line from the midpoint of $\overline{AC}$ to vertex $B$.

5. If the triangle is made up of many thin segments parallel to $\overline{DE}$, each of them will have its center of gravity along the path of point $F$, and therefore the

center of gravity of the triangle as a whole should also lie somewhere along this path.

6. A median of a triangle is a line segment drawn from the midpoint of a side to the opposite vertex; or a median of a triangle is the path traced out by the center of gravity of a line segment moved parallel to one of its sides.

7. Connect the midpoint of a side to its opposite vertex.

8. The medians are always concurrent at the centroid.

## CONJECTURE: THE PROPERTIES OF THE CENTROID

9. $\overline{AD}$; $\overline{BF}$; $\overline{CE}$; point $G$.

10. The centroid divides each median in the ratio $2:1$.

11. The six small triangles all have the same area.

## EXPLAINING

12. $\overline{EG} \parallel \overline{AH}$ (and $EG = \frac{1}{2}AH$), since $E$ and $G$ are the respective midpoints of sides $AB$ and $HB$ of $\triangle ABH$.

13. Similarly, $\overline{DG} \parallel \overline{CH}$ (and $DG = \frac{1}{2}CH$).

14. Therefore, $AHCG$ is a parallelogram (opposite sides parallel (and equal)).

15. Diagonals $AC$ and $GH$ bisect each other (property of parallelograms).

16. Therefore, $F$ bisects $\overline{AC}$, and $\overline{BF}$ is also a median.

17. $FG = \frac{1}{2}HG$, but $HG = GB$ (construction), and therefore $FG = \frac{1}{2}GB$; that is, point $G$ divides the median $FB$ in the ratio $2:1$. Similarly for the other medians.

18. Equal bases and heights.

19. Area $AFB =$ area $CFB$ (same bases and heights).

20. Area $ABG =$ area $CBG$ (area $AFB -$ area $AFG =$ area $CFB -$ area $CFG$).

21. The areas of triangles $CDG$, $BDG$, $BEG$, and $AEG$ are all equal.

22. Similarly, area $ABG$ can be shown to be equal to area $ACG$, and therefore all six small triangles have the same area. (Students should be informed that although it may be good practice to write out the

argument showing area $ABG$ equal to area $ACG$ in full, it is common mathematical practice, for the sake of brevity, not to do so.)

## Present Your Explanation

This section provides students with the opportunity to organize and present their explanations clearly.

## Further Exploration

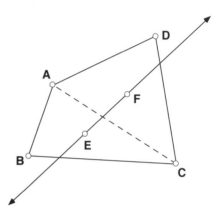

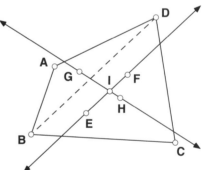

1. a. The center of gravity of a cardboard quadrilateral $ABCD$ can be located by first constructing the centroids $E$ and $F$ of triangles $ABC$ and $ADC$ (see above). The center of gravity of the quadrilateral as a whole must now lie on the line connecting $E$ and $F$. Next, construct the centroids $G$ and $H$ of triangles $ABD$ and $BDC$. As before, the center of gravity of the quadrilateral as a whole must now lie on the line connecting $G$ and $H$. Therefore, the center of gravity is located at $I$, namely, where the two lines $EF$ and $GH$ intersect.

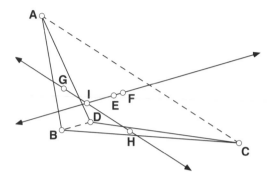

b. The center of gravity *I* of a concave cardboard quadrilateral can sometimes fall outside it, as shown in the figure. (In order to balance such a figure, one would have to attach its center of gravity to the figure with thin wires or rods— compare a wheel with spokes.)

c. The center of gravity of a cardboard pentagon can be found by dividing it into a quadrilateral and a triangle and drawing a line through their respective centers of gravity. Next, divide it into any other quadrilateral and triangle, and again draw the line connecting their respective centers of gravity. The center of gravity of the pentagon as a whole is then located where these two lines meet.

This method can be generalized to any polygon by subdividing it into two paired sets of polygons of lower order. If two lines are then drawn connecting the respective centers of gravity of each pair of polygons, the center of gravity of the polygon as a whole is determined by the intersection of these two lines. (To locate the centers of gravity of higher-order polygons in Sketchpad, it is useful to build up a series of custom tools as you progress from quadrilaterals to pentagons, etc.)

2. The reason the "Fosbury flop" is most effective can be explained in terms of geometry. Suppose, for example, that a high jumper has enough energy to vertically displace his or her center of gravity by 7 ft. Then, using the traditional "scissors" and "straddle" techniques, this high jumper would have to move his or her center of gravity over the high bar, implying that the jumper would probably not be able to jump much higher than 6 ft 10 in. (see first figure). However, using the "Fosbury flop," the body assumes a shape (similar to a concave figure) whose center of gravity actually moves outside the body. In other words, if the same high jumper used the "Fosbury flop," the jumper's center of gravity could pass under the bar while his or her body went over it (see second figure). Using this technique, the same high jumper could therefore possibly jump 7 ft 2 in.—a gain of 4 inches: enough for a gold medal and a new Olympic record!

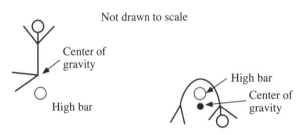

Not drawn to scale

3. a. The average value of abscissa and ordinates of the vertices are equal to the value of the abscissa and ordinate of the centroid.

b. Note that generally speaking, analytic (coordinate) proofs tend to be less *explanatory* than synthetic geometry proofs, and therefore tend more to serve a *verification* function.

Consider the following figure. The midpoint of $\overline{AB}$ has coordinates $\left(\frac{x_1 + x_2}{2}, \frac{y_1 + y_2}{2}\right)$. We shall now use the useful result from coordinate geometry that a point that divides a segment $AB$ with coordinates $A(x_1, y_1)$ and $B(x_2, y_2)$ into the ratio $m : n$ has coordinates

$$\left(x_1\left(\frac{n}{m+n}\right) + x_2\left(\frac{m}{m+n}\right), y_1\left(\frac{n}{m+n}\right) + y_2\left(\frac{m}{m+n}\right)\right)$$

Since the centroid divides segment $CX$ into the ratio $2:1$, the coordinates of the centroid can be determined as follows:

$$\left(x_3\left(\tfrac{1}{3}\right) + \left(\tfrac{x_1 + x_2}{2}\right)\left(\tfrac{2}{3}\right),\ y_3\left(\tfrac{1}{3}\right) + \left(\tfrac{y_1 + y_2}{2}\right)\left(\tfrac{2}{3}\right)\right)$$

$$= \left(\frac{2x_3 + 2x_1 + 2x_2}{6},\ \frac{2y_3 + 2y_1 + 2y_2}{6}\right)$$

$$= \left(\frac{x_1 + x_2 + x_3}{3},\ \frac{y_1 + y_2 + y_3}{3}\right)$$

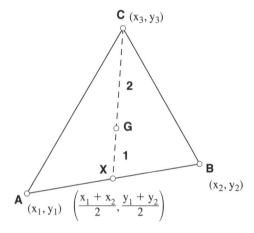

Another approach is to assume that $(x_1, y_1)$ is placed at $(0, 0)$ and $(x_2, y_2)$ at $(x_2, 0)$. Then, by determining the equations of two of the medians, we can locate the centroid by solving this pair of simultaneous equations. This approach, however, involves quite tedious algebra.

c. Note that averaging the coordinates is equivalent to finding the center of gravity of three point masses with equal weight, situated at the vertices. Although this averaging method is easily generalized, it does *not* provide the center of gravity of a cardboard polygon (except for a triangle), but the center of gravity of equal point masses placed at the vertices. For example, the following diagram shows the center of gravity $I$ of a "cardboard" quadrilateral. If, however, only point masses of equal weight are placed at the same vertices, their center of gravity is located at $P$, which clearly does not coincide with $I$.

A: $(-8.184, -0.635)$
D: $(-0.212, 3.210)$
C: $(2.222, -3.281)$
B: $(-6.421, -2.611)$

$$\frac{x_B + x_C + x_D + x_A}{4} = -3.149$$

$$\frac{y_B + y_C + y_D + y_A}{4} = -0.829$$

P: $(-3.149, -0.829)$
I: $(-2.485, -0.636)$

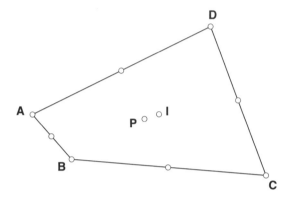

A purely geometric method for locating the point $P$ is shown in the next diagram (from **Quad Centroid.gsp**). Determine the respective centroids $E$, $F$, $G$, and $H$ of triangles $ABC$, $BCD$, $CDA$, and $DAB$. Then quadrilateral $EFGH$ is similar to quadrilateral $DABC$, with a reduction factor of 3, and the lines connecting corresponding vertices are concurrent at the center of the similarity, which is the center of gravity of equal point masses placed at the vertices. A proof of the similarity of these two quadrilaterals and the concurrency of the lines can be found in Yaglom (1962, 21) or de Villiers (1996, 189).

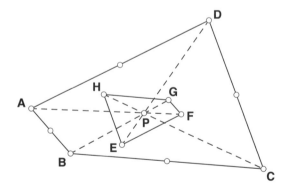

## Alternative Explanation for Median Concurrency

An alternative explanation will now be given; you could present it to students to illustrate the discovery function of proof, since it leads to an immediate generalization of the result, namely Ceva's theorem. (See **Ceva.gsp** and **Ceva Concurrency.gsp**.) Some students may have difficulty in step 2 understanding the reasoning involving the application of the *dividendo* rule. It may help to give students some practical examples, such as $\frac{9}{12} = \frac{3}{4} = \frac{9-3}{12-4} = \frac{6}{8}$, and so on.

Consider again this conjecture: *The three medians of any triangle always meet in one point (are concurrent).*

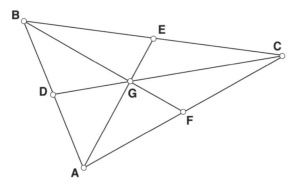

1. Let $\overline{AE}$ and $\overline{CD}$ be medians intersecting at point $G$. Join $B$ with $G$ and extend to $F$ on $\overline{AC}$. We must now show that $F$ is the midpoint of $\overline{AC}$ (in other words, that $\overline{BF}$ is also a median and therefore that all three meet in the same point $G$).

2. If we denote the area of triangle $ABC$ by the notation $(ABC)$, we have

$$\frac{(BAF)}{(BFC)} = \frac{\frac{1}{2}h_1 AF}{\frac{1}{2}h_1 FC} = \frac{AF}{FC} \text{ and } \frac{(GAF)}{(GFC)} = \frac{\frac{1}{2}h_2 AF}{\frac{1}{2}h_2 FC} = \frac{AF}{FC}$$

Therefore, $\dfrac{AF}{FC} = \dfrac{(BAF)}{(BFC)} = \dfrac{(GAF)}{(GFC)}$

$$= \frac{(BAF) - (GAF)}{(BFC) - (GFC)} = \frac{(BAG)}{(BCG)} \cdots$$

dividendo.

Similarly, we find $\dfrac{CE}{BE} = \dfrac{(ACG)}{(BAG)}$ and $\dfrac{BD}{AD} = \dfrac{(BCG)}{(ACG)}$.

3. But it is given that $BE = EC$ and $AD = DB$. Therefore, $(BCG) = (ACG)$ and $(ACG) = (BAG)$, which implies $(BAG) = (BCG)$. But the areas of these two triangles are proportional to $AF$ and $FC$, as shown by the second equation. Thus, $\frac{AF}{FC} = 1$ implies $AF = FC$ and completes the explanation.

## Looking Back

Now encourage your students to look back carefully at the proof. Let them consider the product of the three ratios $\frac{AF}{FC}$, $\frac{AD}{DB}$, and $\frac{BE}{CE}$ expressed in terms of areas in step 2. Ask them what they notice about this product, and whether in deriving these three ratios the properties that $E$ and $D$ are midpoints were used at all. Further, ask them what they can therefore conclude from this.

You can then point out that

$$\frac{AF}{FC} \times \frac{AD}{DB} \times \frac{BE}{CE} = \frac{(BAG)}{(BCG)} \cdot \frac{(ACG)}{(BAG)} \cdot \frac{(BCG)}{(ACG)} = 1$$

and that the properties that $E$ and $D$ are midpoints were not used at all in this derivation. Therefore, we can immediately generalize that if, in any triangle, $\times$ line segments $AD$, $BF$, and $CE$ are concurrent (with $D$, $F$, and $E$ respectively on sides $BC$, $AC$, and $AB$), then $\frac{AF}{FC} \times \frac{AD}{DB} \times \frac{BE}{CE} = 1$. The converse of this result is also true and can be proved by using proof by contradiction.

This interesting result is called Ceva's theorem, after an Italian mathematician named Giovanni Ceva, who published it in 1678. In his honor, the line segments $AE$, $BF$, and $CD$ joining the vertices of a triangle to any given points on the opposite sides are called *cevians*. (Note that apart from the medians, the altitudes and angle bisectors of a triangle can be considered cevians if they are extended to meet the opposite sides.) Although it is not known exactly how Ceva discovered this result, it is likely that he discovered it logically in a fashion similar to that outlined above, and not by using construction and measurement.

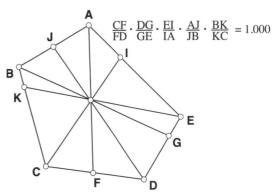

$$\frac{CF}{FD} \cdot \frac{DG}{GE} \cdot \frac{EI}{IA} \cdot \frac{AJ}{JB} \cdot \frac{BK}{KC} = 1.000$$

Interestingly, Ceva's theorem can also be generalized to polygons (see Grünbaum and Shepherd 1995), and you may wish to demonstrate it to your students. (See **Ceva Pentagon.gsp.**) However, for polygons with an even number of sides, this generalization does not deal with the ratios into which the cevians divide the opposite sides, but rather with the ratios into which the cevians divide the diagonals.

## KITE MIDPOINTS (PAGE 59)

The main purpose of this worksheet is to show the discovery function of a logical argument; that is, to show how by explaining something and identifying its underlying characteristic property, we can sometimes immediately generalize the result. You should emphasize that although the generalization in Question 16 could have been discovered by experimentation, the generalization in Question 18 could hardly have been: Who would have thought of trying a quadrilateral with perpendicular diagonals?

**Prerequisites:** Knowledge of properties of parallelograms, rectangles, squares, and kites.

**Sketch: Kite.gsp.**

### CONJECTURE

1. It has (at least) one axis of symmetry through a pair of opposite angles, two pairs of adjacent sides equal, perpendicular diagonals, and so on.

2. *EFGH* is a rectangle.

3. Yes, it is still a rectangle.

4. Yes, when the diagonals are equal.

### EXPLAINING

5. The midsegment of a triangle is parallel to, and equal to half of, the base of the triangle.

*Note:* Students should verify that the arguments below also apply to the concave case, because it is generically different (one of the diagonals falls outside).

6. $\overline{EF} \parallel \overline{AC}$ (and $EF = \frac{1}{2}AC$). (*E* and *F* are midpoints of sides *AB* and *BC*.)

7. $\overline{HG} \parallel \overline{AC}$ (and $HG = \frac{1}{2}AC$). (*H* and *G* are midpoints of sides *AD* and *DC*).

8. $\overline{EF} \parallel \overline{HG}$; $EF = HG$.

9–11. Similarly to Questions 6–8, $\overline{EF} \parallel \overline{HG}$; $EF = HG$. Let students write it out fully, but point out that for reasons of economy, it is customary to say "Similarly, it follows . . ."

12. *EFGH* is a parallelogram, since opposite sides are parallel (or one pair of opposite sides are equal and parallel).

13. Since $\overline{EF}$ and $\overline{HG}$ are parallel to $\overline{AC}$, and $\overline{EH}$ and $\overline{FG}$ are parallel to $\overline{BD}$, $\overline{AC} \perp \overline{BD}$ implies that the pairs of opposite sides of *EFGH* are all perpendicular to each other; that is, all angles are 90°. Therefore, *EFGH* is a rectangle.

14. If *AC* = *BD*, all the sides of *EFGH* are equal, which means it is a square.

### DISCOVERING

15–16. No. *ABCD* therefore need not be a kite for *EFGH* to be a parallelogram, so this result (known as Varignon's theorem) would be true for any quadrilateral.

17–18. No. *ABCD* therefore need not be a kite for *EFGH* to be a rectangle, so this result would be true for any quadrilateral with perpendicular diagonals.

19. The discovery function of a logical explanation.

**CHALLENGE** First construct two perpendicular lines, and then construct points on these lines as vertices for the quadrilateral. Note that this quadrilateral is surprisingly flexible: It can be dragged into convex, concave, and crossed forms.

## LOGICAL DISCOVERY (PAGE 63)

As mentioned in the introductory paragraph of the student sheet, the purpose of this activity is to show students that new results in mathematics are sometimes discovered logically rather than just by construction and measurement.

**Prerequisites:** Students need to know that the length of a triangle midsegment is half the length of the corresponding base. They discover this property in the activity Kite Midpoints.

### DISCOVERING

1. $EF + HG = AC$.

2. $EH + FG = BD$.

3. In $\triangle ABC$, $EF$ is half $AC$, since $E$ and $F$ are midpoints of sides $AB$ and $BC$. Similarly, $HG$ is half $AC$ in $\triangle ADC$. Therefore, $EF + HG = AC$. In the same way, the equation in Question 2 can be derived.

4. Perimeter $EFGH = EF + HG + EH + FG = AC + BD$; that is, the perimeter of the inscribed parallelogram is equal to the sum of the diagonals of the original quadrilateral.

### CHECK BY CONSTRUCTION

Encourage your students to check whether the result is also true for concave and crossed quadrilaterals (they may find this rather surprising) and to verify that these cases can be explained in a similar way.

Apart from stressing the value and power of logical reasoning in predicting in advance the outcomes of practical construction and measurement, such empirical/experimental testing gives concrete meaning to the results. Such testing is often also valuable in that it can provide us with counterexamples for certain special cases, which may necessitate a reformulation of the result or of its logical explanation (proof).

## ISOSCELES TRAPEZOID MIDPOINTS (PAGE 65)

As with the Kite Midpoints activity, the main purpose here is to show the discovery function of a logical argument (explanation); that is, to show how by explaining something and identifying its underlying characteristic property, we can sometimes immediately generalize the result. Emphasize that the generalization in Question 13 would hardly have been discovered by random trial-and-error experimentation: Who would have thought of trying a quadrilateral with equal diagonals?

**Prerequisites:** Students need to know that the length of a triangle midsegment is half the length of the corresponding base. They discover this property in the activity Kite Midpoints. Students should also know properties of parallelograms, rectangles, squares, and kites.

**Sketch: Iso Trap Mdpts.gsp.**

### CONJECTURE

1. The quadrilateral has (at least) one line of symmetry though a pair of opposite sides, (at least) one pair of opposite sides equal, (at least) one pair of opposite sides parallel, and so on.

2. The midpoint quadrilateral $EFGH$ is a rhombus.

3. Yes, when the diagonals are perpendicular to each other.

4. Yes, $EFGH$ is still a rhombus, and when the diagonals are perpendicular, it is a square.

### EXPLAINING

*Note:* Students should verify that the arguments below also apply to the crossed case, because it is generically different (both diagonals fall outside).

5. $\overline{EF} \parallel \overline{AC}$ (and $EF = \frac{1}{2}AC$). ($E$ and $F$ are midpoints of sides $AB$ and $BC$.)

6. $\overline{HG} \parallel \overline{AC}$ (and $HG = \frac{1}{2}AC$). ($H$ and $G$ are midpoints of sides $AD$ and $DC$.)

7. $\overline{EF} \parallel \overline{HG}$, since both are parallel to $\overline{AC}$.

8–10. Similarly to 5–7, $\overline{EH} \parallel \overline{FG}$. Let students write it out fully, but point out that for economical reasons, it is customary to say "Similarly, it follows . . ."

11. Since *EF* and *HG* are equal to $\frac{1}{2}AC$, and *EH* and *FG* are equal to $\frac{1}{2}BD$, $AC = BD$ implies that all the sides of *EFGH* are equal; that is, it is a rhombus.

12. If $\overline{AC} \perp \overline{BD}$, the two pairs of opposite sides of *EFGH* are perpendicular to each other. So all the angles are equal, which means that the rhombus becomes a square.

## DISCOVERING

13. No, we used only the property that it has equal diagonals. No other property of an isosceles trapezoid was used. Therefore, *ABCD* need not be an isosceles trapezoid for the midpoint quadrilateral *EFGH* to be a rhombus. The result would be true for any quadrilateral with equal diagonals.

14. Any quadrilateral with equal diagonals.

15. Carefully reflecting on logical explanations.

**CHALLENGE** A quadrilateral with equal diagonals can be constructed by first constructing a line segment, and then two circles with equal diameters. The endpoints of the diameters are the vertices of the quadrilateral. This construction can be used to drag the quadrilateral into convex, concave, and crossed forms.

### Duality

It might be useful to point out to students the *angle-side* duality demonstrated by the two activities Kite Midpoints and Isosceles Trapezoid Midpoints. For example, the rectangle and rhombus are duals—the rectangle's angles are all equal and the rhombus's sides are all equal. The kite and isosceles trapezoid are also each other's duals, as illustrated in the following table:

| Isosceles trapezoid | Kite |
|---|---|
| Two pairs of equal adjacent *angles* | Two pairs of equal adjacent *sides* |
| One pair of equal opposite *sides* | One pair of equal opposite *angles* |
| Circumscribed circle (*cyclic*) | Inscribed circle (*circum* quad) |
| An axis of symmetry through one pair of opposite *sides* | An axis of symmetry through one pair of opposite *angles* |

## LOGICAL DISCOVERY: CIRCUM QUAD (PAGE 68)

The purpose of this worksheet is to show students that new results in mathematics are sometimes discovered logically rather than always first by construction and measurement.

**Prerequisites:** Tangents to a circle are equal.

**Sketches: Circum Quad.gsp.** Additional sketches are **Concave Circ Quad.gsp, Circum Quad Converse.gsp,** and **Circum Hexagon.gsp.**

### DISCOVERING

1. The distances are equal: $AP = AS$.

2. Similarly, $BP = BQ$, $CQ = CR$, and $DR = DS$.

3. $AB + CD = a + b + c + d$.

4. $BC + AD = b + c + a + d = a + b + c + d$.

5. $AB + CD = BC + AD$.

6. The sums of the two pairs of opposite sides of a circum quadrilateral are equal.

7. *ABCD* would be a kite.

### CHECK BY CONSTRUCTION

Encourage your students to check whether the result is also true for concave and crossed quadrilaterals (they may find this rather surprising) and to verify that these cases can be explained in a similar way.

Apart from stressing the value and power of logical reasoning in predicting in advance the outcomes of practical construction and measurement, such empirical/experimental testing gives concrete meaning to the results. Such testing is also often valuable in that it can provide us with counterexamples for certain special cases, which might necessitate a reformulation of the result or of its logical explanation (proof).

### Further Exploration

1. The angle bisectors are concurrent at the center of the incircle. The explanation is simple: The incenter is equidistant from all four sides (the radii of the incircle are perpendicular to the quadrilateral's sides). But

each angle bisector is the locus of all points equidistant from its two adjacent sides. Therefore, each angle bisector must pass through the incenter.

Conversely, this is a necessary condition for any polygon to be circumscribed around a circle. (For example, for a polygon to have an incircle, it must have a point that is equidistant from all the sides. Therefore, the angle bisectors must be concurrent.)

2. It's possible to drag to obtain special cases such as a (general) kite, a (general) rhombus, or a square.

3. By constructing the intersection of the tangential lines as in the first figure shown, we can obtain a concave circum quad in which the extensions of two sides are now tangent to the incircle. Suppose we label the tangent segments as before; then $AB + CD = (a + b) + (d - c)$ and $BC + AD = (b - c) + (a + d)$, which are clearly equal. A sample sketch is given in **Concave Circ Quad.gsp.**

$DA = 14.363$ cm
$BC = 4.092$ cm
$DA + BC = 18.46$ cm
$DC = 6.910$ cm
$AB = 11.545$ cm
$DC + AB = 18.46$ cm

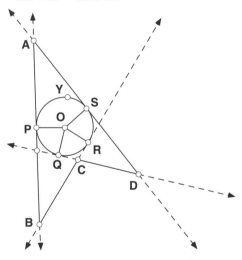

You may wish to encourage even further exploration by asking your students how they would try to generalize the result to other polygons.

Both the convex and concave cases can also be generalized to certain types of $2n$-gons ($n > 1$) in which the two sums of *alternate* sides are equal. A sample sketch is shown in the second figure and is given in **Circum Hexagon.gsp.**

$a = 4.504$ cm
$c = 4.197$ cm
$y = 4.250$ cm
$a + c + y = 12.951$ cm
$x = 4.173$ cm
$z = 4.957$ cm
$b = 3.822$ cm
$x + z + b = 12.951$ cm

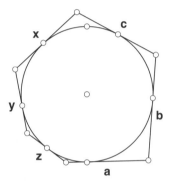

The following theorem in this regard is proved in de Villiers (1993; 1996, 183–187):

> If $A_1 A_2 \ldots A_{2n}$ ($n > 1$) is any circumscribed $2n$-gon in which vertex $A_i \rightarrow A_{i+k}$ (vertex $A_i$ is joined to $A_{i+k}$), the two sums of alternate sides are equal (where $k$ is the total turning we would undergo by walking around the perimeter of the polygon).

You may want to encourage your students to investigate whether the converse of the circum quadrilateral result for the sides is also true. That is, is a quadrilateral with the two sums of opposite sides equal necessarily a circum quadrilateral? A sketch called **Circum Quad Converse.gsp** is provided to assist such an investigation. To prove the converse, you can use proof by contradiction (see de Villiers 1996). Note that the converse is true only for quadrilaterals; it is not, in general, true for $2n$-gons.

## Duality

The *angle-side* duality referred to in the Teacher Notes for the Isosceles Trapezoid Midpoints activity is also neatly displayed between the circum and cyclic quadrilaterals. For example, in the circum quadrilateral, the two sums of opposite sides are equal, whereas in the cyclic quadrilateral, the two sums of opposite angles are equal. The square and the parallelogram are self-dual in relation to these two concepts, as shown in the following tables.

| Square | |
|---|---|
| Circumscribed circle (cyclic) | Inscribed circle (circum quad) |
| An axis of symmetry through each pair of opposite sides | An axis of symmetry through each pair of opposite angles |

| Parallelogram | |
|---|---|
| Equal opposite angles | Equal opposite sides |
| No circumscribed circle | No inscribed circle |

Using this angle-side duality, the quadrilaterals can be classified as shown. Note that the vertical line of symmetry can be used to find the dual of any particular quad by reflection in it. For a more detailed discussion of this duality, consult de Villiers (1996).

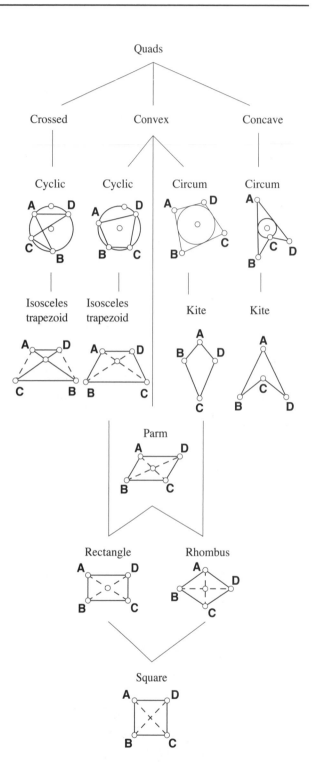

## AREAS (PAGE 73)

The purpose of this worksheet is to caution students not to make generalizations too quickly; they must be sure to explore many different variations, in particular looking at special or borderline cases. Students who don't test extreme cases can be led (or misled) to a false conjecture by the sketch.

At the beginning, check that the measurement and calculation accuracy in the Preferences is set to units (because students are then more likely to make the false conjecture). You can use this activity to introduce the verification (checking) function of proof. Point out that this activity illustrates that there are some cases in which it's difficult to really be sure that an empirical check has been sufficient.

The second page of the activity is optional. Once students have discovered that their conjectures are not true in general, in the second part of the activity they discover a special case (a parallelogram) in which it is true.

**Prerequisites:** None.

**Sketches: Areas.gsp** and **Areas 2.gsp.**

## CONJECTURE

1. $5 : 1$.

2. Probably yes.

3. Students will probably make the conjecture that the ratio of the given areas is always $5 : 1$.

4. Answers will vary.

Area ABCD = 43.0 cm$^2$
Area IJKL = 8.6 cm$^2$
$\dfrac{\text{Area ABCD}}{\text{Area IJKL}} = 5.0$

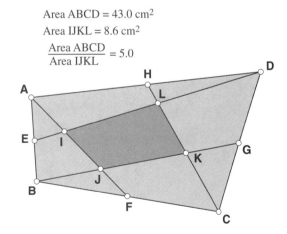

Area ABCD = 37.0 cm$^2$
Area IJKL = 7.1 cm$^2$
$\dfrac{\text{Area ABCD}}{\text{Area IJKL}} = 5.2$

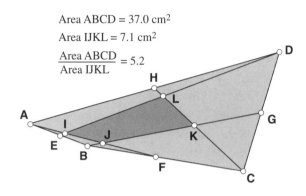

**CHALLENGE** With the ratio between the areas of the two quadrilaterals shown by $\frac{\text{Area } ABCD}{\text{Area } IJKL}$, it is hardly likely that students would come up with counterexamples. You could even suggest to your students to try more accurate measurement and calculation. Some students may, however, become bothered by their inability to construct an explanation and may begin to suspect that the result is not generally true.

5. $5 : 1$.

6. Yes.

7. In a parallelogram $ABCD$ with $E$, $F$, $G$, and $H$ the respective midpoints of $\overline{AB}$, $\overline{BC}$, $\overline{CD}$, and $\overline{DA}$ the ratio of the area of $ABCD$ to the area of the quadrilateral formed by $\overline{AF}$, $\overline{BG}$, $\overline{CH}$, and $\overline{DE}$ is $5 : 1$.

8. Answers will vary.

## EXPLAINING

Since the figure as a whole has half-turn symmetry, $IJKL$ has half-turn symmetry as well and is therefore also a parallelogram. The half-turns of the indicated triangles create four parallelograms, each congruent to $IJKL$ and surrounding it. Therefore, Area $ABCD$ : Area $IJKL = 5 : 1$.

### An Update

The quadrilateral $IJKL$ is called a *midvexogram* by Winicki-Landman (2001). The conjecture by Sylvie Penchaliah mentioned in the Acknowledgments, namely, that the ratio of the area of a (convex) quadrilateral to that of its midvexogram is always greater than or equal to 5 (also mentioned in Keyton 1997) was proven in 1999 by three mathematicians from the University of Kentucky—Avinash Sathaye, Carl Eberhart, and Don Coleman. Using the symbolic processing ability of Maple, they have also shown that this ratio is precisely 5 when the midvexogram is a trapezoid and that in all other cases the ratio is always less than 6 (although there are quadrilaterals for which this ratio can be as close to 6 as wanted). Their paper can be downloaded from http://www.ms.uky.edu/~carl/coleman/coleman2.html.

This proof, though convincing, is hardly explanatory, and the problem of finding a short, elegant, and explanatory geometric proof remains open.

## VARIGNON AREA (PAGE 76)

This activity follows the Areas activity, and it is expected that students will be a bit more skeptical here about their Sketchpad observations and thus more motivated to seek additional verification or conviction. The focus of this activity is therefore on introducing the verification function of proof.

**Prerequisites:** The Kite Midpoints activity or knowledge of the result that the line connecting the midpoints of two sides of a triangle is parallel to the third side and half its length. Properties of parallelograms. Conditions for congruency.

**Sketch: Varignon Area.gsp.**

## CONJECTURE

1. *EFGH* is a parallelogram. (This is true even for concave and crossed cases.)

2. The area of the parallelogram is half that of the original quadrilateral.

3. No.

4. No.

5. The midpoints of the sides of a quadrilateral form a parallelogram.

6. Responses will vary.

## PROVING

7. $\overline{EF} \parallel \overline{AC} \parallel \overline{HG}$, since *E* and *F* are midpoints of sides *AB* and *CB* in triangle *ABC* and *H* and *G* are midpoints of sides *AD* and *CD* in triangle *ADC*.

8. $\overline{EH} \parallel \overline{BD} \parallel \overline{FG}$ (same reasons).

9. $\overline{EF} \parallel \overline{HG}$ and $\overline{EH} \parallel \overline{FG}$, so opposite sides are parallel, and therefore *EFGH* is a parallelogram. Another way of proving it is to note in Question 7 that not only is $\overline{EF} \parallel \overline{HG}$, but since both *EF* and *HG* are equal to half *AC*, they are also equal to each other. So one pair of opposite sides are equal and parallel, from which it follows that *EFGH* is a parallelogram.

*Note:* You may also wish to ask your students to prove that the result is also true in the concave and crossed cases. The proofs are similar, except that now one or both diagonals fall outside.

10. There are four triangles lying outside *EFGH*, namely, *AEH*, *DHG*, *CGF*, and *BFE*.

11. The sum of the areas of these triangles must be equal to the area of *EFGH*.

12. The translated quadrilateral is congruent to *EFGH* (property of translation), so it is also a parallelogram with area equal to that of *EFGH*.

13. $\triangle\,EBF$ is congruent to $\triangle\,F'CF$ (SAS).

14. $FB = FC$ (*F* is midpoint of *BC*); $FE = FF'$ (corresponding sides of translated parallelograms), and $m\angle\,EFB = m\angle\,F'FC$ (directly opposite angles).

15. $\triangle\,HDG$ is congruent to $\triangle\,G'CG$ (SAS).

16. Similar to Question 14.

17. $\triangle\,AEH$ is congruent to $\triangle\,CF'G'$ (SSS).

18. From Question 13, we have $CF' = BE$ and $BE = AE$. Therefore, $AE = CF'$. Similarly, from Question 17, we have $AH = CG'$. Also, $EH = FG$ (corresponding sides of translated parallelograms).

19. *FGC* is common to both *ABCD* and *FGG'F'*. Therefore, the sum of the areas of the triangles is equal to that of *FGG'F'*, and therefore to that of *EFGH*.

## Present Your Proof

This section provides an opportunity for students to synthesize the argument and write it up in a coherent way.

## Further Exploration

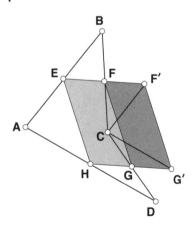

This proof is a little tricky. In the concave case, only three triangles, namely *AEH*, *DHG*, and *BFE*, fall within *ABCD*. The remaining triangle *CGF* now falls outside *ABCD*. If we use the notation $(XYZ)$ to represent the area of a polygon $XYZ$, then $(ABCD) = (AEH) + (BFE) + (DHG) + (EFGH) - (CGF) = (AEH) + (BFE) + (DHG) - (CGF) + (EFGH)$. In other words, we now have to prove that $(AEH) + (BFE) + (DHG) - (CGF) = (EFGH)$. From the translation, *EFGH* is still congruent to *FGG'F'*. As before, triangles *EBF* and *F'CF*, triangles *HDG* and *G'CG*, and triangles *AEH* and *CF'G'* are congruent. But if we subtract the area of triangle *CGF* from the sum of the areas of triangles *G'CG*, *CF'G'*, and *F'CF*, we obtain the area of parallelogram *FGG'F'*, which is equal to that of *EFGH*.

## Alternative Proof

There are several different ways of proving this result. It might be instructive for your students to work through hints such as those given here.

## Hints

1. Express the area of *EFGH* in terms of the area of *ABCD* and the areas of triangles *AEH*, *CFG*, *BEF*, and *DHG*.

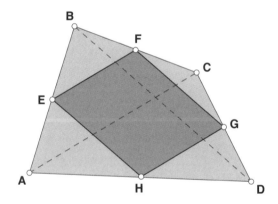

2. Drop a perpendicular from *A* to $\overline{BD}$ and express the area of triangle *AEH* in terms of the area of triangle *ABD*.

3. Similarly, express the areas of triangles *CFG*, *BEF*, and *DHG*, respectively, in terms of the areas of *CBD*, *BAC*, and *DAC*, and substitute in step 1.

4. Simplify the equation in step 3 to obtain the desired result.

## Proof

1.  Using the notation $(XYZ)$ for the area of a polygon $XYZ$, we have $(EFGH) = (ABCD) - (AEH) - (CFG) - (BEF) - (DHG)$.

2.  If the height of $\triangle ABD$ is $h$, then $(ABD) = \frac{1}{2}BD \cdot h$ and $(AEH) = \frac{1}{2}\left(\frac{1}{2}BD\right) \cdot \frac{1}{2}(h) = \frac{1}{4}(ABD)$, or simply, the base and the height are half those of the large triangle.

3.  $(EFGH) = (ABCD) - \frac{1}{4}(ABD) - \frac{1}{4}(CBD) - \frac{1}{4}(BAC) - \frac{1}{4}(DAC)$.

4.  $(EFGH) = (ABCD) - \frac{1}{4}(ABCD) - \frac{1}{4}(ABCD)$
    $= \frac{1}{2}(ABCD)$.

### Further Discussion

You may also want your students to work through an explanation for the concave case, because it is generically different. For example, unless the notation is carefully reformulated (e.g., see crossed quadrilaterals below), the equation in step 1 of the proof does not hold in the concave case, but becomes $(EFGH) = (ABCD) - (AEH) - (CFG) - (BEF) + (DHG)$ (see below). However, substituting into this equation as before, and simplifying, leads to the same conclusion.

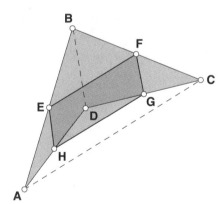

### Crossed Quadrilaterals

It is also true for the crossed quadrilateral $ABCD$ that $EFGH$ has half its area, as some of your students may have found on Sketchpad. However, the proof is even more tricky and first requires consideration of what we mean by the area of a crossed quadrilateral. Let us now first carefully try to define a general area formula for convex and concave

quadrilaterals. It seems natural to define the area of a convex quadrilateral to be the sum of the areas of the two triangles into which it is decomposed by a diagonal. For example, diagonal $\overline{AC}$ decomposes the area as follows (see first figure): $(ABCD) = (ABC) + (CDA)$.

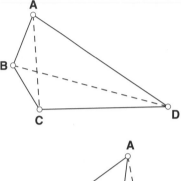

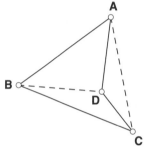

In order to make this formula work for the concave case as well (see second figure), we obviously need to define $(CDA) = -(ADC)$. In other words, we can regard the area of a triangle as being *positive* or *negative* depending on whether its vertices are named in *counterclockwise* or *clockwise* order. For example:

$$(ABC) = (BCA) = (CAB) =$$
$$-(CBA) = -(BAC) = -(ACB)$$

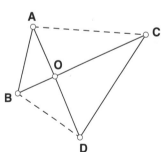

Applying the above formula and definition of area in a crossed quadrilateral (see figure), we find that diagonal $AC$ decomposes its area as follows:

$$(ABCD) = (ABC) + (CDA) = (ABC) - (ADC)$$

In other words, this formula forces us to regard the "area" of a crossed quadrilateral as the difference between the areas of the two small triangles $ABO$ and $ODC$. (Note that diagonal $BD$ similarly decomposes $(ABCD)$ into $(BCD) + (DAB) = -(DCB) + (DAB)$). An interesting consequence of this is that a crossed quadrilateral will have zero "area" if the areas of triangles $ABO$ and $ODC$ are equal.

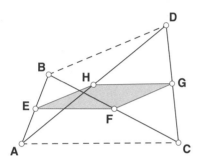

Using this valuable notation, the result can now simultaneously be proved for all three cases (convex, concave, and crossed) as follows:

$$(EFGH) = (ABCD) - (AEH) - (FCG) - (EBF) - (DHG)$$

$$= (ABCD) - \frac{1}{4}(ABD) - \frac{1}{4}(CDB) - \frac{1}{4}(BCA) - \frac{1}{4}(DAC)$$

$$= (ABCD) - \frac{1}{4}(ABCD) - \frac{1}{4}(ABCD)$$

$$= \frac{1}{2}(ABCD)$$

## LOGICAL PARADOX (PAGE 80)

This worksheet is based on an example that has often been used (wrongly) to try to motivate a need for proof among students. Basically, students are told that this example illustrates that diagrams may be deceiving and therefore unreliable. Consequently, reliance only on experimental evidence is unreliable and we thus require formal proof.

However, this example actually illustrates the importance of making (reasonably) *accurate* diagrams when constructing proofs, rather than showing that diagrams are unreliable. In fact, the false conclusion that all triangles are isosceles shows how easily a correct logical argument can lead to a fallacy because of a construction error, or a mistaken assumption, in a sketch. Instead of motivating a need for proof, such examples actually emphasize the importance of experimental testing (i.e., the *accurate* construction of some examples), noting with care the relative positions of points, lines, and so on that are essential to the proof. Although a French mathematician once said "Geometry is the art of drawing correct conclusions from incorrectly drawn sketches," this example dramatically shows that they should not be constructed too incorrectly!

**Prerequisites:** Knowledge of conditions for congruency.

**Sketch: Paradox.gsp** (This sketch should be given to students only at the end of the worksheet, after they have worked through the logical argument based on the faulty diagram.)

## CONJECTURE

1. Triangles $CGD$ and $CGF$ are congruent (SAA).

2. $DG = FG$.

3. $AG = BG$, since $G$ lies on the perpendicular bisector of $\overline{AB}$.

4. Triangles $GDA$ and $GFB$ are congruent (90°, S, S).

5. $DA = FB$.

6. $CD = CF$.

7. $CD + DA = CA = CF + FB = CB$.

8. Therefore, $ABC$ is isosceles.

## REFLECT/CHECK

Although the argument itself is quite correct, the problem arises from an incorrectly drawn sketch. For example, when we actually construct this diagram in Sketchpad (or with paper and pencil), the point *G* always falls outside, and one of the points *D* or *F* always falls *inside* the triangle while the other falls *outside*, and therefore invalidates the "proof," as the diagram below demonstrates. (Note that if it is given that *CA* = *CB*, the angle bisector of angle *C* and the perpendicular bisector of *AB* coincide and there is no unique point *G*.)

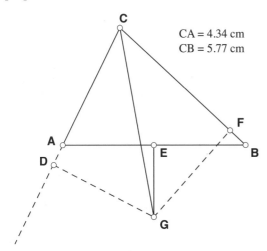

CA = 4.34 cm
CB = 5.77 cm

The experimental observation that *G* always falls outside and that *one* of the points *D* or *F* always falls *inside* the general triangle while the other falls *outside* is proved in Movshovitz-Hadar and Webb (1998, 74–75). It is also possible to construct a simpler argument based on symmetry, starting with the assumption that *ACB* is isosceles, with *AC* = *BC*, and then considering what happens if C is moved to the left or the right of the perpendicular bisector of $\overline{AB}$.

## CYCLIC QUADRILATERAL CONVERSE (PAGE 82)

Following the Areas activity, in which students are introduced to a false result, this worksheet focuses on further elaborating the verification function of a proof. In other words, it can be used to convince or to remove lingering doubts. However, it is important that you not yet present proof at this stage to your students as the *only* accepted means of verification in mathematics. Instead it should be emphasized as an *additional* or *complementary* path to verification/conviction.

**Prerequisites:** Cyclic Quadrilateral activity. Knowledge of exterior angle theorem for a triangle.

**Sketch: Cyclic Quad.gsp.** An additional sketch is **Cyclic Quad 2.gsp.** (In this dynamic sketch, a quadrilateral *EFGH* has been constructed with opposite angles *HEF* and *HGF* supplementary by constructing them respectively equal to angles *DCA* and *DCB* lying adjacent to each other on a straight line. The sketch shows that the perpendicular bisectors are always concurrent and that a circumcircle always passes through all four vertices.)

### Answers to Introductory Questions

Its opposite angles are supplementary.

The converse: If the opposite angles of a convex quadrilateral are supplementary, the quadrilateral is cyclic.

### CONJECTURE

1. Quadrilateral *ABCD* is cyclic.

2. The sketch appears to support the formulated converse.

3. Responses may vary.

CHALLENGE  Responses may vary, but it is anticipated that not all students will be entirely convinced that the conjecture is always true and that this will create a need for additional verification (that is, a logical proof).

## PROVING

4. $m\angle ABC + m\angle AD'C = 180°$, since $D'$ lies on the constructed circle.

5. $m\angle ABC + m\angle ADC = 180°$ is given.

6. Therefore, $m\angle AD'C = m\angle ADC$.

7. $m\angle AD'C = m\angle D'CD + m\angle ADC$.

8. But since $m\angle AD'C = m\angle ADC$, it implies that $m\angle D'CD$ must be equal to zero. Therefore, $D$ and $D'$ coincide, and $ABCD$ must be cyclic.

9. The argument is similar to the preceding one, except that now $m\angle ADC = m\angle DCD + m\angle AD'C$.

### Further Discussion

Note that if directed angles are used as discussed in the activities Crossed Quadrilateral Sum and Cyclic Quadrilateral, the sums of the measures of two pairs of opposite angles in a crossed cyclic quadrilateral are both equal to 360° (see below). Therefore, the converse could be formulated as follows: If in a crossed quadrilateral the sums of the measures of its two pairs of opposite angles (angles $D$ and $F$, and angles $C$ and $E$) are equal (to 360°), then it is cyclic.

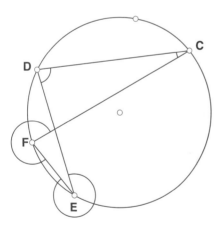

The above formulation is equivalent to the condition that the acute angles at opposite vertices $D$ and $F$, or the acute angles at opposite vertices $C$ and $E$, are equal. This can be proved for a convex quadrilateral in a way similar to the above proof.

Consider the crossed quadrilaterals, where it is given that opposite angles $B$ and $D$ are equal. Draw the circumcircle

of triangle $ABC$. Assume that this circle does not pass through $D$ so that we have one of the two cases below. Label the intersection of ray $AD$ with the circle as $D'$ and consider the argument below.

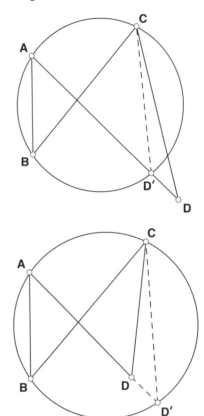

### Proof

1. $m\angle ABC = m\angle AD'C$, since $D'$ lies on the constructed circle.

2. But $m\angle ABC = m\angle ADC$ is given.

3. Therefore, $m\angle AD'C = m\angle ADC$.

4. In the first case, $m\angle AD'C = m\angle D'CD + m\angle ADC$, and in the second case, $m\angle ADC = m\angle DCD' + m\angle AD'C$.

5. But since $m\angle AD'C = m\angle ADC$, this implies that $m\angle D'CD$ is equal to zero. Therefore, $D$ and $D'$ coincide.

As mentioned in the Teacher Notes for the Cyclic Quadrilateral activity, for certain types of cyclic $2n$-gons where $n > 1$, the two sums of the sets of alternate angles are equal. (For convex ones, these sums are equal to $180°(n - 1)$.) Note, however, that the converse of this result is true only for a quadrilateral ($n = 2$), and that it is not necessarily true for a hexagon. For example, consider the hexagon $ABCDEF$, where $m\angle A + m\angle C + m\angle E = m\angle B + m\angle D + m\angle F$, but the hexagon is not cyclic because the perpendicular bisectors of its sides are not concurrent.

$$m\angle FAB + m\angle BCD + m\angle DEF = 360°$$
$$m\angle ABC + m\angle GDE + m\angle EFA = 360°$$

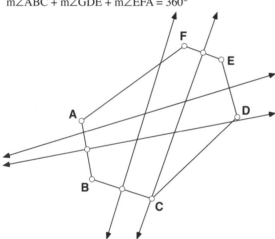

## CONCURRENCY (PAGES 85)

This activity is intended to caution students to not make generalizations too quickly and to carefully search for possible counterexamples. In other words, even if some result appears to be visually true on Sketchpad, they should still be skeptical. From this experience, students should also become more aware that in some cases, additional justification in the form of a logical argument (proof) is necessary before we can safely say that something is really always *true*. The next activity (Triangles Altitudes) will therefore build on this experience to emphasize the verification function of proof.

**Prerequisites:** None.

**Sketch: Concurrency.gsp.**

## CONJECTURE

1. It is the centroid (point of concurrency of the medians).

2. They are the incircles of three triangles formed by two medians and an adjacent side of the triangle.

3. The three lines appear to be always concurrent (particularly if the line widths of $\overline{AE}$, $\overline{BF}$, and $\overline{CD}$ are "thick").

4. Responses may vary.

**CHALLENGE**   The conjecture is not true, as shown on the next page. It is important that students realize that in mathematics only one counterexample is needed to disprove a conjecture. Note that even for an acute triangle, the result is false, since a counterexample can also be found easily by enlarging the figure sufficiently, either by dragging or by using a dilation.

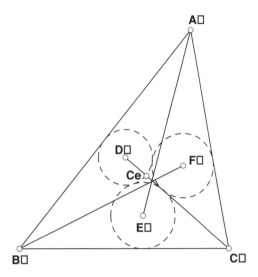

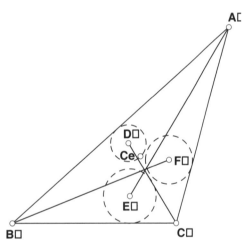

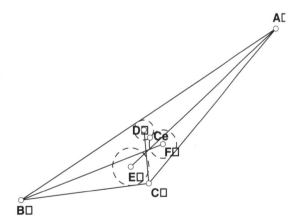

## TRIANGLE ALTITUDES (PAGE 86)

This worksheet follows the Concurrency activity and explicitly focuses on the verification function of proof.

**Prerequisites:** Water Supply I and II, Cyclic Quadrilateral, Concurrency, and Cyclic Quadrilateral Converse activities. Knowledge of the properties of cyclic quads (equal angles on same chord or opposite angles supplementary implies quad is cyclic) and the concurrency of the perpendicular bisectors of a triangle.

**Sketch: Altitudes.gsp.**

### CONJECTURE

1. The altitudes are always concurrent.

2. Responses may vary.

**CHALLENGE** It is important for you, as the teacher, to take a neutral stand here, or even better that of a skeptic, and not to indicate to the students that the result is indeed true. Challenge them to convince you or other skeptics in the class.

### PROVING

3. Responses may vary, but students are intended to recognize the verification function of proof in this quotation.

4. The altitudes are $\overline{AE}$, $\overline{BF}$, and $\overline{CD}$. $\overline{GI} \parallel \overline{BC}$, $\overline{IH} \parallel \overline{AB}$, and $\overline{GH} \parallel \overline{AC}$.

5. *GBCA* is a parallelogram, since its opposite sides are parallel.

6. *GA = BC* (opposite sides of parm).

7. *ABCI* is a parallelogram, since its opposite sides are parallel.

8. *AI = BC* (opposite sides of parm).

9. *GA = AI.*

10. $m\angle\, GAE = 90° = m\angle\, IAE$, since $\overline{AE}$ is perpendicular to $\overline{BC}$ and $\overline{GI}$ is parallel to $\overline{BC}$.

11. $\overline{GI}$ has been constructed parallel to $\overline{BC}$.

12. $\overline{AE}$ is the perpendicular bisector of $\overline{GI}$.

13. Yes, $\overline{BF}$ and $\overline{CD}$ are also the perpendicular bisectors of sides *GH* and *HI* of triangle *GHI*.

14. Since the perpendicular bisectors of any triangle are concurrent, $\overline{AE}$, $\overline{BF}$, and $\overline{CD}$ are concurrent. But these lines are also the altitudes of triangle *ABC*, and are therefore concurrent.

## Present Your Proof

This section provides students with the opportunity to organize the proof as a coherent whole.

## Alternative Proofs

It may also be informative for students to encounter the following well-known proof for the concurrency of the altitudes. Here, two altitudes, $\overline{AE}$ and $\overline{BF}$, are drawn, and it must now be shown that the line *CD* from the remaining vertex through their point of intersection *O* is also an altitude.

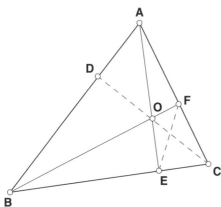

*OECF* is cyclic, since the opposite angles at *F* and *E* measure 90°. *ABEF* is also cyclic, since $m\angle AFB = 90° = m\angle AEB$ on segment *AB*. Angle *OEF* = angle *OCF* (angles on chord *OF* of *OECF*). But angle *OEF* = angle *ABF* (angles on chord *AF* of *ABEF*). Therefore, angle *OCF* = angle *ABF*, which implies that *DBEF* is cyclic (angle *DBO* = angle *DCF* on segment *DF*). Thus, $m\angle BDO = 90°$, since it is supplementary to its opposite angle *BEO* in cyclic quad *DBOE*.

## LIGHT RAY IN A TRIANGLE (PAGE 90)

This activity follows the Triangle Altitudes activity, although it can be done independently from that activity if students already know about the concurrency of the altitudes of a triangle.

**Prerequisites:** Knowledge of properties of cyclic quads (e.g., that equal angles on same chord or opposite angles supplementary implies that quad is cyclic).

**Sketch: Light Ray.gsp.**

## CONJECTURE

1. Angle *XYB* = angle *ZYC* and angle *YZC* = angle *XZA*, but angles *AXZ* and *BXY* are not necessarily equal.

2. These two pairs of angles are equal because of the reflections occurring on sides *BC* and *AC*. For any reflection, the angle of incidence is equal to the angle of reflection.

3. They (appear to) coincide with the feet of the altitudes. (The triangle with minimum perimeter of an acute triangle is found at the feet of the altitudes.)

4. All three pairs of angles around the feet of the altitudes are equal.

5. Yes, it is also true.

6. Responses may vary.

**CHALLENGE** It is important for you, as the teacher, to take a neutral stand here, or even better that of a skeptic, and not to indicate to the students that the result is indeed true. Challenge them to convince you or other skeptics in the class.

## PROVING ANGLE MEASURES EQUAL

7. The opposite angles are supplementary ($m\angle OEC = 90° = m\angle OFC$).

8. Since $\angle OEC$ and $\angle OFC$ are both right angles, they can both be inscribed in semicircles; therefore, *OECF* is a cyclic quadrilateral.

9. $m\angle EOC = m\angle EFC$ (on chord *EC*).

10. Opposite angles are supplementary ($m\angle ADO = 90° = m\angle AFO$); therefore, $ADOF$ is a cyclic quad.

11. $m\angle AFD = m\angle AOD$ (on chord $AD$).

12. $m\angle EOC = m\angle AOD$, since they are directly opposite.

13. Therefore, $m\angle EFC = m\angle AFD$. (Note that their complementary angles, $BFE$ and $BFD$, are therefore also equal.)

14. Responses may vary.

## Notes

It is possible to come up with several different variations on the above proof, and students may find it useful to compare their efforts. It may be instructive for students to repeat the above proof for the cases in which triangle $ABC$ is right or obtuse.

## PROVING MINIMUM PERIMETER

15. $XY_1' = XY$ and $Y_2'Z = ZY$ from the reflections.

16. The two paths are equal in length.

17. $X$, $Z$, and $Y_2'$ are always collinear. Explanation: $m\angle XZA = m\angle YZC$ (from the construction used to model the situation), but $m\angle YZC = m\angle Y_2'ZC$ (from the reflection around $AC$). Therefore, $m\angle XZA = m\angle Y_2'ZC$. Since $AC$ is given as a straight line, $m\angle XZA + m\angle XZC = 180°$. Therefore, $m\angle Y_2'ZC + m\angle XZC = 180°$; thus, $XZY_2'$ is also a straight line ($X$, $Z$, and $Y_2'$ are collinear).

18. The path $XY_1' + ZX + ZY_2'$ will be a minimum when it is a straight line. Therefore, $X$ must be positioned so that $m\angle AXZ = m\angle BXY_1'$ (vertically opposite angles must be equal).

19. $m\angle BXY_1' = m\angle BXY$ (from the reflection around $AB$). So if the condition in Question 18 ($m\angle AXZ = m\angle BXY_1'$) is met, $m\angle AXZ = m\angle BXY$.

20. For triangle $XYZ$ to have minimum perimeter, the following three pairs of angles must be equal: $m\angle AXZ = m\angle BXY$, $m\angle BYX = m\angle CYZ$, and $m\angle XZA = m\angle YZC$. But from the first result, we have the three pairs of angles surrounding the feet of pedal triangle $DEF$ equal; that is, $m\angle DFA = m\angle EFC$, $m\angle FDA = m\angle EDB$, and $m\angle DEB = m\angle FEC$. Therefore, triangle $XYZ$ must coincide with the pedal triangle $DEF$. (Or, alternatively, pedal triangle $DEF$ meets this criterion of having the angles surrounding its feet equal; therefore triangle $XYZ$ must coincide with the pedal triangle $DEF$.)

*Note:* The above argument shows that the feet of the pedal triangle meet the criterion, and thus provides a solution, but does not show the uniqueness of this solution. A complete proof that the triangle with minimum perimeter lies only at the feet of the altitudes can be found in Hildebrandt and Tromba (1985, 60–63).

© 2003 Key Curriculum Press

# PARALLEL LINES (PAGE 95)

This worksheet also focuses on emphasizing the verification function of proof, since most people tend to find it rather surprising that the parallel lines will always return to the original starting point. Intuitively, most people guess that it would depend on the position of *D*, and that in some cases we can carry on parallel lines indefinitely without their returning to their starting point. The discovery, therefore, seems a little counterintuitive, which makes it a good context for emphasizing the verification function of proof.

**Prerequisite:** None.

**Sketch: Parallel.gsp.**

## CONJECTURE

1. $\overline{ED} \parallel \overline{CA}$.

2. $\overline{EF} \parallel \overline{BA}$.

3. $\overline{FG} \parallel \overline{BC}$.

4. Responses will vary.

5. We need only go around twice (i.e., draw six parallel lines) before we return to *D*.

6. Responses may vary.

**CHALLENGE**  It is important for you, as the teacher, to take a neutral stand here, or even better that of a skeptic, and not to indicate to the students that the result is indeed true. Challenge them to convince you or other skeptics in the class.

## PROVING

7. The parallel lines divide adjacent sides into equal ratios. (This result will be proved later on, in Chapter 5.)

8. $\dfrac{BD}{DA} = \dfrac{BE}{EC} = \dfrac{AF}{FC} = \dfrac{AG}{GB} = \dfrac{CH}{HB} = \dfrac{CI}{IA} = \dfrac{BJ}{JA}$

9. $\dfrac{BD}{DA} = \dfrac{BJ}{JA}$; therefore, *J* must coincide with *D*.

## Further Exploration

1. The result still holds, even if point *D* lies on the extension of the side *AB*, in which case the other points will also lie on the extensions of the other sides.

2. In a pentagon, we also need only go around twice (draw 10 lines) to return to our starting point (see below). The proof is similar to the preceding one.

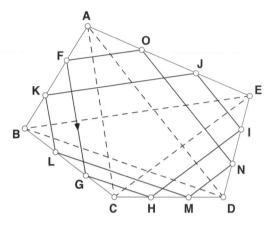

3. The result is generalizable to any polygon with an odd number of vertices. A precise formulation and a general proof is given in de Villiers (1996, 83–85), as well as a similar result for polygons with an even number of vertices.

## Related Results

You might also ask your students to measure the areas and perimeters of the hexagon and compare it with the original triangle. They will then discover that the ratio of the area of the hexagon *DEFGHI* to that of triangle *ABC* is also constant for a fixed position of the starting point *D* (see figures on the following page). A proof of this result is given in de Villiers (1999b), but requires a definition of the area of crossed polygons, which would probably be beyond most high school students. (See the discussion regarding the area of a crossed quadrilateral in the Teacher Notes for the Varignon Area activity.)

On the other hand, the perimeter of the hexagon *DEFGHI* is always equal to that of triangle *ABC*, irrespective of the position of *D;* this is very easy to prove.

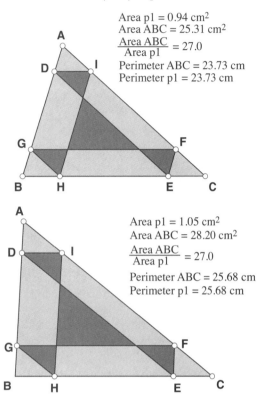

Area p1 = 0.94 cm²
Area ABC = 25.31 cm²
$\frac{\text{Area ABC}}{\text{Area p1}} = 27.0$
Perimeter ABC = 23.73 cm
Perimeter p1 = 23.73 cm

Area p1 = 1.05 cm²
Area ABC = 28.20 cm²
$\frac{\text{Area ABC}}{\text{Area p1}} = 27.0$
Perimeter ABC = 25.68 cm
Perimeter p1 = 25.68 cm

# PARALLELOGRAM ANGLE BISECTORS

## (PAGE 101)

This worksheet follows up on some of the earlier worksheets by presenting proof as a means of explanation, verification, and discovery. Students are given slightly less direction in constructing proofs so that they can gradually become more independent.

**Prerequisites:** Knowledge of congruency, properties of parallel lines and rectangles. For the optional Further Exploration section at the end, knowledge of the properties of cyclic quadrilaterals is also required (e.g., from the Cyclic Quadrilateral and Cyclic Quadrilateral Converse activities in this book).

**Sketch: Parallelogram.gsp.** An additional sketch is **Quad Bisectors.gsp.**

## CONJECTURE

1. Opposite sides are parallel.

2. *EFGH* is a rectangle.

3. *EFGH* becomes a square (has all sides equal) when *ABCD* is a rectangle.

4. *EFGH* becomes a point.

5. *EFGH* becomes a point.

**CHALLENGE** This provides students with an opportunity to attempt their own proofs.

## PROVING *EFGH* IS A RECTANGLE

6. $m\angle AHG = 180° - x - y$ (sum of the measures of the angles of triangle *AHB*).

7. They are supplementary, since $\overline{AD} \parallel \overline{BC}$.

8. $2x + 2y = 180°$, which simplifies to $x + y = 90°$.

9. $m\angle AHG = 180° - (x + y) = 180° - 90° = 90°$.

10. Yes, the other angles are also 90°, and therefore *EFGH* is a rectangle.

## PROVING *EFGH* IS A SQUARE WHEN *ABCD* IS A RECTANGLE

11. $FD = FC$, since $m\angle FDC = 45° = m\angle FCD$.

12. Triangles *DAE* and *CBG* are congruent (SAA).

13. Therefore, $ED = GC$.

14. $FD - ED = FC - GC$; therefore, $FE = FG$.

15. A rectangle with one pair of adjacent sides equal is a square.

## Further Exploration

1. The angle bisectors of a rhombus coincide with its diagonals, which meet in only one point.

2. The additional sketch **Quad Bisectors.gsp** could be used for this exploration. The angle bisectors of any quadrilateral form a cyclic quadrilateral (provided it is not a circum quadrilateral, that is, circumscribed around a circle, since its angle bisectors are obviously concurrent). Students should be able to work from the preceding argument to prove this observation (for the convex case) as follows.

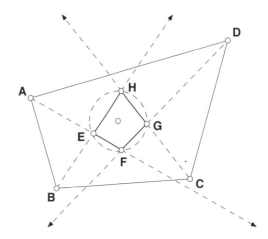

### Proof (Convex)

$$m\angle BHC = 180° - \left(\frac{1}{2}\angle B + \angle C\right) \text{ and}$$

$$m\angle AFD = 180° - \left(\frac{1}{2}\angle A + \frac{1}{2}\angle D\right)$$

Therefore,

$$\angle BHC + \angle AFD = 360° - \frac{1}{2}\left(\angle A + \angle B + \angle C + \angle D\right)$$

$$= 360° - 180° = 180°$$

Therefore, *EFGH* is a cyclic quad.

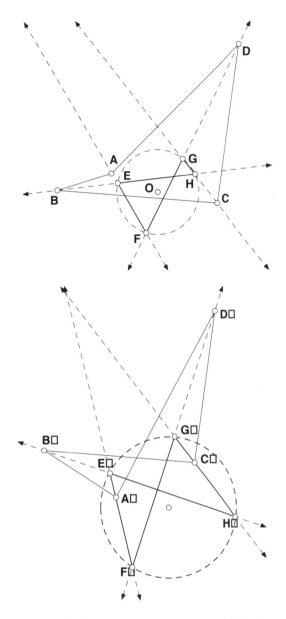

In a case in which *ABCD* is concave or crossed, *EFGH* becomes a crossed quadrilateral, so the proofs need to be adapted using directed angles and require knowledge of the properties of crossed quadrilaterals (for a proof, see de Villiers 1996, 191–192).

## PARALLELOGRAM SQUARES (PAGE 104)

This activity reinforces the idea that constructing a logical explanation (proof) can be perceived as an intellectual challenge after a result is found to be true experimentally. This activity can also be done later if you feel that it may be too challenging for students at this stage.

**Prerequisites:** Side-angle-side condition for congruent triangles; symmetry properties of parallelograms, rhombuses, and squares, as well as their hierarchical relationships.

**Sketch: Para Squares.gsp.** Additional sketches are **Aubel 1.gsp** and **Aubel 2.gsp.**

### CONJECTURE

1. They are squares.

2. It is a parallelogram.

3. *EFGH* is a square.

4. Yes, it remains a square.

5. Yes, it remains a square. Note that the squares now lie on the "inward" sides of the parallelogram.

### INVESTIGATING FURTHER

6. The whole configuration maps onto itself under a half-turn, and therefore *EFGH* must also be a parallelogram. (A parallelogram is the only quadrilateral with half-turn symmetry.)

7. Triangles *HAE* and *HDG* are congruent.

8. 90°.

9. $m\angle EHG = 90°$, since $\overline{GH}$ is rotated onto $\overline{EH}$.

### PROVING

10. $m\angle HAE = 90° + m\angle BAD$, since $m\angle HAD$ and $m\angle EAB$ both equal 45°.

11. $m\angle BAD + m\angle ADC = 180°$, since they are co-interior angles between the two parallels $\overline{AB}$ and $\overline{DC}$.

12. $m\angle HDG = 360° - (45° + 45° + m\angle ADC)$

$$= 360° - (90° + 180° + m\angle BAD)$$

$$= 90° + m\angle BAD.$$

13. Therefore, $m\angle HAE = m\angle HDG$.

14. $EA = GD$, since squares $E$ and $G$ are congruent (on opposite sides of parallelogram).

15. $AH = DH$ (property of a square).

16. Triangles $HAE$ and $HDG$ are congruent (SAS), and therefore $HE = HG$.

17. Therefore, $EFGH$ is a rhombus (a parallelogram with two equal adjacent sides is a rhombus).

18. $m\angle AHD = 90°$ (diagonals of a square are perpendicular to each other).

19. Therefore, a rotation of 90° maps $\overline{DH}$ onto $\overline{AH}$, and thus triangle $HDG$ onto $EAH$. Thus, $m\angle EHG$ must also be 90°. (Or, alternatively, $m\angle AHD = 90° = m\angle AHE + m\angle EHD$. But from congruency, $m\angle AHE = m\angle DHG$, and therefore $m\angle DHG + m\angle EHD = \angle EHG$.)

20. Therefore, $EFGH$ is a square (a rhombus with a right angle is a square).

In the above explanation (proof), a number of properties are used that students may have encountered previously, but not yet logically explained (proved). This should not present a problem if they later revisit these properties and logically establish them.

Although the above proof uses an elegant argument, some students may find it easier to simply repeat the same argument about corresponding pairs of congruent triangles at vertices $B$, $C$, and $D$. This implies that all four sides are equal (a rhombus), but since the one right angle is already proved, it follows that the quadrilateral must be a square.

## Further Exploration

1. The result still holds if the squares are constructed inwardly, and exactly the same argument applies, except that both $m\angle HAE$ and $m\angle HDG$ are then equal to $m\angle D = 90°$.

2. The centers of the squares on the sides of an isosceles trapezoid form a kite. This follows directly from symmetry; that is, the axis of symmetry of the isosceles trapezoid is also the axis of symmetry of the formed quadrilateral that passes through one pair of opposite vertices (which implies that it is a kite).

3. The centers of the squares on the sides of a kite form an isosceles trapezoid. This also follows directly from symmetry, as in the preceding argument.

## Generalizing

You may wish to encourage students to investigate/explain what would happen if they constructed squares on the sides of any quadrilateral. In general, the diagonals of $EFGH$ are equal and perpendicular ($\overline{EG} \perp \overline{HF}$) in any quadrilateral (see Yaglom 1962, 39 or Kelly 1966).

The latter result, known as van Aubel's theorem, can be further generalized for similar rectangles and rhombuses on the sides as shown below (different proofs are given in de Villiers 1997 and 1998a). In the first figure, $\overline{EG}$ is always perpendicular to $\overline{FH}$. Also, $\overline{KM}$ is congruent to $\overline{LN}$ where $K$, $L$, $M$, and $N$ are the midpoints of the line segments joining adjacent vertices of the similar rectangles as shown. A dynamic sketch is provided in **Aubel 1.gsp.**

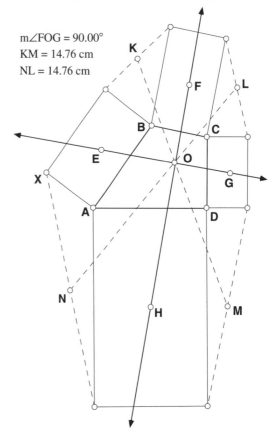

In the second figure, $\overline{EG}$ is always congruent to $\overline{FH}$. Also, $\overline{KM}$ is perpendicular to $\overline{LN}$, where K, L, M, and N are the midpoints of the line segments joining adjacent vertices of the similar rhombuses as shown. A dynamic sketch is provided in **Aubel 2.gsp.** The "intersection" of these two results therefore yields van Aubel's theorem.

Two interesting special cases are obtained by constructing these similar rectangles and rhombuses on the sides of a parallelogram. In the first case, a rhombus is obtained, and in the second case, a rectangle. Proofs of these two special cases can be found in de Villiers (1996, 101–102).

All these results also nicely display the angle-side duality mentioned in the Teacher Notes for the Isosceles Trapezoid Midpoints activity, as well as in the Teacher Notes for the Logical Discovery: Circum Quad activity.

These two generalizations involving similar rectangles and rhombuses on the sides of any quadrilateral have since been generalized further to parallelograms, and to points other than the "centers" (see de Villiers 2000). A downloadable copy of this paper, as well as Sketchpad 3 sketches illustrating these generalizations, can be found on the author's Web site at http://mzone.mweb.co.za/residents/profmd.

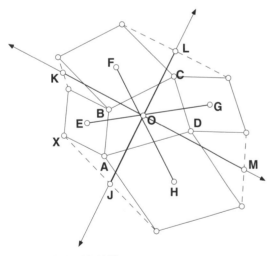

m∠LOM = 90.000°
EG = 8.402 cm
FH = 8.402 cm

# THE FERMAT-TORRICELLI POINT (PAGE 108)

This activity reinforces the function of proof discussed earlier, namely, logical discovery. After proving the results for a right triangle, students focus their attention on whether the arguments are still valid if angle ABC is not a right angle. This should make them realize that the result is immediately generalizable to *any* triangle. You can emphasize that this often happens in mathematical research, namely, that in proving some result, we find on reflection that some conditions were never used in the proof (i.e., were unnecessary) and that the result can therefore be generalized. The reason for starting with the right triangle is therefore to specifically illustrate this *discovery* function of proof.

**Prerequisites:** Knowledge of the properties of convex cyclic quadrilaterals (quadrilaterals that can be inscribed in a circle). Specifically, students should know that a convex quadrilateral is cyclic if and only if a pair of its opposite angles are supplementary. These properties have been discovered and proved in two earlier activities: Cyclic Quadrilateral and Cyclic Quadrilateral Converse. Also, students should be familiar with the SAS method of proving a pair of triangles congruent.

**Sketch: Fermat 1.gsp.** Additional sketches are **Fermat 2.gsp, Fermat 3.gsp,** and **Fermat 4.gsp.**

## CONJECTURE

1. The "outer" triangles are all equilateral. If students are uncertain, encourage them to measure the sides or angles.

2. The lines DC, EA, and FB are concurrent.

3. The line segments DC, EA, and FB are equal in length.

4. The triangles lie inward.

5. Both results are still true.

**CHALLENGE**  This gives students a first try at writing a proof for their conjectures.

## VERIFYING

6. Triangle DBC maps onto triangle ABE (and they are therefore congruent).

7. The six angles around $O$ all measure 60°.

8. They are supplementary, which implies that quadrilateral $AOBD$ is a cyclic quadrilateral (a quadrilateral that can be inscribed in a circle).

9. The circumcircles of the other two outer triangles also pass through $O$.

**CHALLENGE** After these hints, this challenge provides another opportunity for students to attempt to construct their own proofs.

## PROVING SEGMENTS EQUAL

10. $DB = AB$, because triangle $DBA$ is equilateral.

11. $BC = BE$, because triangle $ECB$ is equilateral.

12. $m\angle DBC = 60° + m\angle ABC = m\angle ABE$.

13. Triangles $DBC$ and $ABE$ are congruent by SAS.

14. $DC = AE$, because corresponding parts of congruent triangles are congruent.

15. Similar to the above.

16. No. Therefore, the argument will still be valid even if $m\angle ABC$ is not 90°; the result is valid for *any* triangle.

17. Responses may vary. Students should notice that the argument they made to defend their conjecture did not require that angle $ABC$ be a right angle. This means that their conjecture was in fact "a special case of a more general one."

## PROVING LINES CONCURRENT

18. The measure of angle $BCE$ is 60°, because triangle $BCE$ is equilateral.

19. $m\angle BOE = m\angle BCE$ (angles on chord $BE$), and therefore $m\angle BOE$ is also 60°.

20. $m\angle BOA = 120°$, because it is supplementary to $\angle BDA$ of cyclic quadrilateral $DBOA$.

21. $m\angle AOE$ is 180°, because $m\angle BOA + m\angle BOE = 120° + 60° = 180°$.

22. Similar to the above.

23. $m\angle AOC = 360° - (m\angle BOA + m\angle BOC) = 360° - 240° = 120°$.

24. $CFAO$ is a cyclic quadrilateral (because opposite angles $AOC$ and $AFC$ are supplementary).

25. Similar to the above.

26. Yes, the argument would still be valid. Therefore, the result is valid for *any* triangle.

27. Responses may vary.

## Further Exploration

An interesting generalization of the concurrency result is the following (shown in the figure):

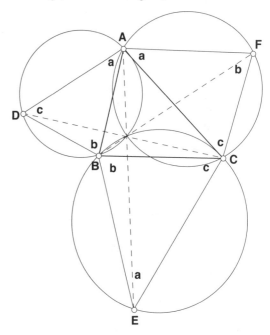

"If similar triangles $DBA$, $CBE$, and $CFA$ are constructed outwardly on the sides of any triangle $ABC$, then segments $DC$, $EA$, and $FB$ are concurrent."

The proof is similar to the one for the special case of equilateral triangles.

This result can be generalized even further as follows, and is shown in the next figure:

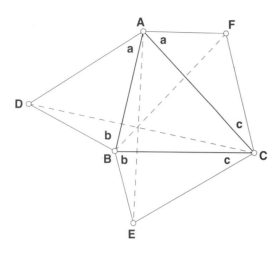

"If triangles *DBA*, *ECB*, and *FAC* are constructed outwardly on the sides of any triangle *ABC* so that *m∠DAB* = *m∠CAF*, *m∠DBA* = *m∠CBE*, and *m∠ECB* = *m∠ACF*, then segments *DC*, *EA*, and *FB* are concurrent."

One proof of this generalization, given in de Villiers (1996), is a little more complicated, using Ceva's theorem. A ready-made sketch called **Fermat 3.gsp**, which illustrates this generalization, is provided. An even further generalization is given and proven in de Villiers (1999a). This involves six triangles and a sketch is given in **Fermat 4.gsp.**

## AIRPORT PROBLEM (PAGE 115)

This activity can be used to reinforce the idea of proof as a means of verification, because students are likely to experience some uncertainty as to the precise location of the optimal point. This activity can be done independently of the preceding activity, The Fermat-Torricelli Point (except for the Looking Back section, which specifically refers to the Fermat-Torricelli point). Furthermore, the solution of this problem does not require knowledge of the properties of cyclic quadrilaterals—a prerequisite for The Fermat-Torricelli Point activity.

If you are planning to do The Fermat-Torricelli Point activity, it is recommended that it precede the Airport Problem. Otherwise, the logical discovery of the generalization from a right triangle to any triangle in The Fermat-Torricelli Point activity may be less surprising.

**Prerequisites:** Students should have some familiarity with transformations, particularly rotations.

**Sketch: Airport.gsp.** Additional sketches are **Airport 2.gsp, Airport 3.gsp, Airport 4.gsp,** and **Airport 5.gsp.**

## CONJECTURE

1. The angle measures are all approximately equal to 120°.

2. Same as Question 1.

3. The optimal point is situated where the measures of angles *ADC*, *BDA*, and *CDB* are all equal to 120°.

4. **Certainty:** Students may have some difficulty noticing that the three angle measures are equal and may not be entirely confident that this is really always the case. This doubt thus provides a good opportunity to again reinforce the idea of proof as a means of verification.

**CHALLENGE** Student responses will vary.

## PROVING

5. *CD* = *CD′*, because they map to each other.

6. Triangle *DCD′* is equilateral (*m∠D′CD* = 60° and *CD* = *CD′*, which imply that *m∠CD′D* and *m∠CDD′* are also both 60°).

7. *D′D* = *DC*.

8. *AD* = *A′D′*, because they map to each other.

9. $AD + CD + BD = A'D' + D'D + DB$.

10. The path $A'D' + D'D + DB$ will be a minimum when it is a straight line.

11. $m\angle A'D'C = 120°$, because $A'D'D$ is a straight line and $m\angle CD'D = 60°$ (from Question 6). Therefore, $m\angle ADC = 120°$, because it maps onto angle $A'D'C$.

12. Similar to Questions 5–11.

## Looking Back

$\overline{AC}$ maps to $\overline{A'C}$, so $m\angle A'CA = 60°$ and $A'C = AC$. Therefore, the other two angles of triangle $A'CA$ also measure 60°, and the triangle is therefore equilateral. Similarly, the other two triangles can be shown to be equilateral.

## Further Exploration

1. Some of the main assumptions are

   • The three cities are roughly the same size (if they weren't, it might be better to place the airport closer to the largest city).

   • The terrain between the cities is flat (that is, no hills or valleys).

   • There are no other natural obstacles such as rivers, swamps, or lakes to avoid.

   • The roads can be built perfectly straight.

   • The three cities lie in the shape of an acute triangle. (Actually more precisely, none of the angles is greater than 120°.)

2. **Theorem:** If triangle $EFG$ is equilateral, then the angles surrounding point $D$ are each 120°.

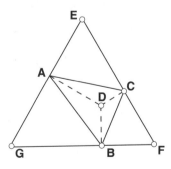

   **Proof:** Quadrilateral $ADBG$ is cyclic, since the opposite angles $GAD$ and $GBD$ are both right angles. But if

triangle $EFG$ is equilateral, then angle $AGB = 60°$ and therefore the opposite angle $ADB = 120°$. In the same way, the other two angles around $D$ can be shown to be equal to 120°.

**Theorem:** If triangle $EFG$ is equilateral, then the sum of the distances from $D$ to $A$, $B$, and $C$ is a minimum.

**Proof:** According to the theorem, the sum of the distances from any point *other than D* would be greater than the sum of the distances from $D$ to the three cities. Let $W$ be any arbitrary point not coinciding with $D$. We now want to prove that $WA + WB + WC > DA + DB + DC$.

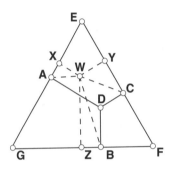

Drop perpendiculars from $W$ to the sides of the equilateral triangle. Then according to the theorem proved in the Distances in an Equilateral Triangle activity $WX + WY + WZ = DA + DB + DC$, but from the triangle inequality $WX < WA$, $WY < WC$, $WZ < WB$. Therefore, $WA + WB + WC > DA + DB + DC$.

Your students may quite rightly ask: Why another proof of the airport theorem? It might help to point out that producing a different proof often helps establish new logical connections with other results and that the purpose is therefore not of further conviction. Indeed, many theorems in mathematics have several different proofs, each providing useful links and valuable insights into why they are true.

3. The airport should be placed at the vertex of the obtuse angle.

4. The airport should be placed at the city in the middle. Similarly, if we have four collinear cities, then the airport can be placed anywhere in the middle segment. In general, for an odd number of collinear cities, the

optimal solution will lie at the middle city, and for an even number of cities, the optimal solution will lie anywhere in the middle segment (see **Airport 3.gsp**).

**Proof:** Note that the sum of distances between any two adjacent cities is always constant, irrespective of where the airport is placed between the two cities. Therefore, when the number of cities is even, the minimum sum would be found by placing the airport in the middle segment, since moving outside the middle segment will increase the sum of the distances to the middle two cities, and therefore the total sum of all the distances. Similarly, it follows that when the number of cities is odd, the optimal position is found at the middle city.

5. The easiest way to solve a problem like this is to "weigh" the distances in proportion to the sizes of the cities. For example, since the largest city is weighed the most, it ensures that the distance to the largest city will be shortened proportionally. To minimize the sum of the distances, we only need to drag $D$ until the expression $6DA + 10DB + 7DC$ becomes a minimum (see **Airport 4.gsp**).

However, a purely geometric solution is possible, and the author will be writing an article in this regard, which will be made available with a Sketchpad 4 sketch at his Web site http://mzone.mweb.co.za/residents/profmd/homepage.html.

6. The optimal solution for a convex quadrilateral will be at the intersection of the diagonals, but for a concave quadrilateral the optimal solution will lie at the vertex forming a *reflex* angle (angle greater than 180°).

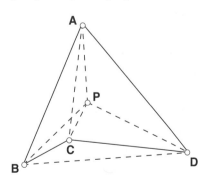

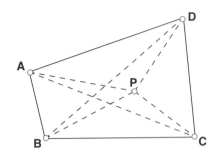

Consider the first figure. If $P$ does not lie on $BD$, then $BP + PD > BD$ since the shortest path between two points is a straight line. Therefore to have $BP + PD$ as short as possible, $P$ must lie somewhere on $BD$. Similarly, we can argue that for $AP + PC$ to be a minimum, $P$ must also lie somewhere on $AC$. Therefore, point $P$ must lie at the intersection of the two diagonals.

Similarly, in the second case, if $P$ does not lie on $AC$, then $AP + PC > AC$ since the shortest path between two points is a straight line. Therefore to have $AP + PC$ as short as possible, $P$ must lie somewhere on $AC$. But since $BD$ in this case lies outside the quadrilateral, $P$ should be placed on $AC$ as close as possible to $BD$, therefore at vertex $C$.

7. If the space coordinates of the four vertices $A$, $B$, $C$ and $D$ are respectively $(x_B, y_B, z_B)$, $(x_C, y_C, z_C)$, and $(x_D, y_D, z_D)$ and that of the airport is $(x, y, z)$, then we just need to minimize the expression

$$\sqrt{(x - x_A)^2 + (y - y_A)^2 + (z - z_A)^2} +$$
$$\sqrt{(x - x_B)^2 + (y - y_B)^2 + (z - z_B)^2} +$$
$$\sqrt{(x - x_C)^2 + (y - y_C)^2 + (z - z_C)^2}$$

Although this would require advanced calculus, we could, if we had a three-dimensional version of Sketchpad, simply drag the point representing the airport until a minimum is obtained.

# NAPOLEON (PAGE 119)

This activity follows on The Fermat-Torricelli Point activity and further explores the properties of the same configuration. However, it is possible to do this activity independently of The Fermat-Torricelli Point activity.

**Prerequisites:** Knowledge of properties of a cyclic quadrilateral. Specifically, students should know that the opposite angles in a cyclic quadrilateral are supplementary, and they should also know the converse. Students should also be familiar with the definition of a kite and the property that its diagonals are perpendicular.

**Sketch: Napoleon.gsp.** Additional sketch is **Napolean 2.gsp.**

## CONJECTURE

1. Triangle *GHI* is equilateral.

2. It remains equilateral.

**CHALLENGE**  This provides students with an opportunity to attempt their own proofs.

## PROVING

3. Quadrilateral *ADBO* is cyclic, because a circle passes through all four of its vertices.

4. Since *DBOA* is cyclic, angle *AOB* and angle *D* are supplementary, and therefore $m\angle AOB = 120°$.

5. *GBHO* is a kite, because $\overline{GB}$ and $\overline{GO}$ are radii of circle *G*, and $\overline{HB}$ and $\overline{HO}$ are radii of circle *H*.

6. $m\angle GKO = 90°$, because the diagonals of a kite are perpendicular.

7. *GOIA* is a kite, since $\overline{GO}$ and $\overline{GA}$ are radii of circle *G*, and $\overline{IO}$ and $\overline{IA}$ are radii of circle *I*.

8. $m\angle GJO = 90°$, because the diagonals of a kite are perpendicular.

9. $m\angle KGJ = 360° - 90° - 90° - 120° = 60°$ (using the fact that the angles of quadrilateral *GJOK* sum to 360°).

10. In the same way, it can be shown that one of the other angles is 60° (implying that the remaining one is also 60°).

## Further Exploration

Students may discover the following two interesting generalizations:

1. If *similar* triangles *DBA*, *BEC*, and *ACF* are erected on the sides of any triangle *ABC*, their circumcenters *G*, *H*, and *I* form a triangle similar to the three triangles.

2. If *similar* triangles *DBA*, *CBE*, and *CFA* are erected on the sides of any triangle *ABC*, their circumcenters *G*, *H*, and *I* form a triangle similar to the three triangles. (Notice that the similar triangles have different orientations in these two different generalizations.)

You may wish to encourage even further exploration by asking students to consider what happens if the angles *D*, *E*, and *F* are arbitrary, but together sum to 180°, because this latter investigation leads to the following generalization:

3. If triangles *DBA*, *BEC*, and *ACF* are erected on the sides of any triangle *ABC* so that $m\angle D + m\angle E + m\angle F = 180°$, their circumcircles meet in a common point, and their circumcenters *G*, *H*, and *I* form a triangle, then $m\angle G = m\angle D$, $m\angle H = m\angle E$, and $m\angle I = m\angle F$ (see figure on the next page).

## Proof

This result can be proved in exactly the same way as for the equilateral triangles earlier. For example, construct circumcircles *ADB* and *BEC* to intersect in *B* and *O* (see figure on the next page). Joining *O* with *A*, *B*, and *C*, we see that $m\angle BOC = 180° - m\angle E$, $m\angle AOB = 180° - m\angle D$, and so on.

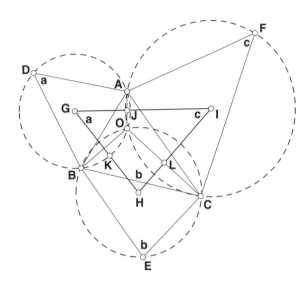

$$m\angle AOC = 360° - (m\angle BOC + m\angle AOB)$$

$$= 360° - (180° - m\angle E + 180° - m\angle D)$$

$$= m\angle E + m\angle D$$

$$= 180° - m\angle F$$

Therefore, $\angle AOC$ and $\angle F$ are supplementary, and $O$ therefore lies on the circumcircle of $\triangle AFC$. Now since $\overline{GH}$, $\overline{HI}$, and $\overline{GI}$ are respectively perpendicular to the common chords $OB$, $OC$, and $OA$, it follows that $OKGJ$, $OKHL$, and $OLIJ$ are all cyclic quadrilaterals. Therefore, $\angle I$ must be the supplement of $\angle AOC$, but from the aforementioned result, we have $\angle F$ also the supplement of $\angle AOC$. Therefore, $\angle I = \angle F$, and in the same way it follows that $\angle G = \angle D$ and $\angle H = \angle E$.

Note that both generalizations (1) and (2), about similar triangles, are simply special cases of generalization (3).

Another interesting version of the first generalization on the previous page is given in **Napoleon 2.gsp** (proofs can be found in de Villiers 1996, 177–181 and King 1997):

4. If *similar* triangles *DBA*, *BEC*, and *ACF* are erected on the sides of any triangle *ABC*, and any three points *P*, *Q*, and *R* are chosen so that they respectively lie in the same positions relative to these triangles, then *P*, *Q*, and *R* form a triangle similar to the three triangles.

| | |
|---|---|
| m∠DAB = 54° | m∠QRP = 54° |
| m∠DBA = 76° | m∠PQR = 76° |
| m∠BDA = 50° | m∠QPR = 50° |

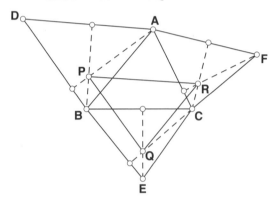

For example, the figure above shows that the respective orthocenters of the similar triangles form another triangle similar to the three exterior triangles. Similarly, the respective centroids and incenters would form a similar triangle.

## MIQUEL (PAGE 122)

This worksheet focuses on further developing students' skills in writing proofs, rather than on the meaning of proof.

**Prerequisites:** Knowledge of the properties of cyclic quads, the AA condition of similarity, and the fact that the diagonals of a kite are perpendicular to each other.

**Sketch: Miquel.gsp.** Additional sketch is **Miguel 2.gsp.**

### CONJECTURE

1. G and H are the centers of circles drawn, respectively, through points A, D, and F and points D, B, and E.

2. The three circles are always concurrent at a point.

3. The centers G, H, and I form a triangle similar to triangle ABC.

**CHALLENGE** This provides students with the opportunity to attempt their own proofs.

### PROVING CIRCUMCIRCLES CONCURRENT

4. $m\angle DOF = 180° - m\angle A$, since ADOF is cyclic.

5. $m\angle DOE = 180° - m\angle B$, since BEOD is cyclic.

6. $m\angle EOF = 360° - (180° - m\angle A + 180° - m\angle B) = m\angle A + m\angle B$ (the sum of the measures of angles around O is 360°).

7. $m\angle EOF = 180° - m\angle C$, since $m\angle A + m\angle B + m\angle C = 180°$.

8. Quadrilateral OECF is cyclic (opposite angles are supplementary).

### PROVING TRIANGLE *GHI* SIMILAR TO TRIANGLE *ABC*

9. GDHO is a kite, since $\overline{GD}$ and $\overline{GO}$ are radii of circle G, and $\overline{HD}$ and $\overline{HO}$ are radii of circle H.

10. $m\angle GJO$ is 90°, since the diagonals of a kite are perpendicular to each other.

11. GOIF is a kite, since $\overline{GO}$ and $\overline{GF}$ are radii of circle G and $\overline{IO}$ and $\overline{IF}$ are radii of circle I.

12. $m\angle GKO$ is 90°, since the diagonals of a kite are perpendicular to each other.

13. Quadrilateral GJOK is cyclic, since opposite angles GJO and GKO are supplementary.

14. $m\angle DOF = 180° - m\angle A$ from the first proof. But angle JGK and angle JOK are opposite angles in cyclic quad GJOK. Therefore, $m\angle JGK = 180° - (180° - m\angle A) = m\angle A$.

15. Follows in the same way.

### Investigate Further

1. The result still holds even if the constructed points lie on the extensions of the sides. Note, however, that the above proof is not general enough to cover the cases in which the points lie on the extensions of the sides or the point of concurrency lies outside the triangle, although it can easily be adapted. For a completely general proof covering all cases, we need to use the idea of directed line segments (for example, see Johnson 1929, 133).

2. Essentially, this is only the converse of Miquel's theorem, as quadrilaterals ADOF, BEOD, and CFOE are all cyclic (exterior angles are equal to opposite interior angles). Furthermore, exactly as before, their circumcircles intersect at O and the three centers of these circles form a triangle similar to triangle ABC.

### Connecting to the Napoleon Generalization

In the Teacher Notes for the Napoleon activity, the following interesting generalization of Napoleon's theorem is mentioned: "If triangles DBA, BEC, and ACF are erected on the sides of any triangle ABC so that $m\angle D + m\angle E + m\angle F = 180°$, their circumcircles meet in a common point, and their circumcenters G, H, and I form a triangle, then $m\angle G = m\angle D, m\angle H = m\angle E$, and $m\angle I = m\angle F$."

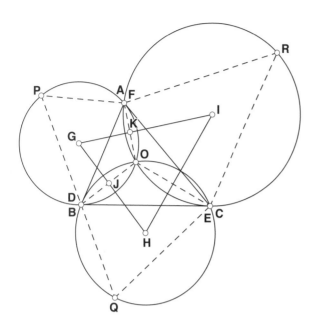

Perhaps surprisingly, this generalization can be viewed as a special kind of limiting case of Miquel's theorem, as follows: In the **Miquel.gsp** sketch, drag *D* to (almost) coincide with *B*, drag *E* to (almost) coincide with *C*, and drag *F* to (almost) coincide with *A*. (Note that technically speaking, none of the circles is uniquely defined if all of these three points coincide exactly with the vertices of triangle *ABC*.)

From Miquel's theorem, we have triangle *GHI* similar to triangle *ABC*, and the circles *G*, *H*, and *I* concurrent at *O*. From the properties of cyclic quadrilaterals, it now follows that any angle *APB* would be equal to angle *G*, any angle *BQC* would be equal to angle *H*, and any angle *CRA* would be equal to angle *I*. But this configuration is equivalent to the above generalization of Napoleon's theorem.

From this formulation, the following converse of the above generalization of Napoleon's theorem is now also apparent: If for any arbitrary point *O* and triangle *ABC*, three circumcircles *AOB*, *BOC*, and *COA* are constructed, and triangles *DBA*, *BEC*, and *ACF* are erected so that *D*, *E*, and *F* are arbitrary points respectively in the arcs *AB*, *BC*, and *CA*, then the circumcenters *G*, *H*, and *I* form a triangle with $m\angle G = m\angle D$, $m\angle H = m\angle E$, and $m\angle I = m\angle F$ (and obviously $m\angle D + m\angle E + m\angle F = 180°$).

## REASONING BACKWARD: TRIANGLE MIDPOINTS (PAGE 129)

This worksheet focuses on the systematization function of proof, since we are here constructing a proof for a result that was earlier discovered and accepted without proof. With the traditional deductive approach, this result and its proof would be presented before its application to results such as Varignon's theorem and kite and isosceles trapezoid midpoints. However, in actual mathematical research, results are seldom discovered in this straightforward linear fashion. For example, we might first discover an interesting result (for example, Varignon's theorem) and then, upon trying to prove it, find that it can be proved in terms of another result (triangle midpoints). Our attention then shifts to proving this other result (the lemma, if you like). In writing up the results and their proofs, it is of course conventional to first prove the lemma and then the main result, but if this is used as a *teaching approach*, it hides the fact that the actual sequence of discovery may have been the other way around. This worksheet attempts to give students some insight into the way a deductive ordering of some results may be arrived at by reasoning backward, rather than pretending that we always have the phenomenal foresight to first prove a particular, relatively uninteresting theorem (or lemma) because we anticipate that it will be used in proving important, interesting results later on.

**Prerequisites:** Kite Midpoints, Isosceles Trapezoid, and Logical Discovery (Varignon) activities in this book, and knowledge of the properties of and conditions for a parallelogram.

**Sketch: Triangle Midpoints.gsp.**

### PROVING

1. *ADCF* is a parallelogram because its diagonals $\overline{AC}$ and $\overline{DF}$ bisect each other.

2. $\overline{FC} \parallel \overline{AD}$ because opposite sides of a parallelogram are equal and parallel.

3. $\overline{FC} \parallel \overline{DB}$ because $AD = DB$ and *ADB* is a straight line. Therefore, *DBCF* is a parallelogram (opposite sides are equal and parallel).

4. $\overline{DF} \parallel \overline{BC}$ because they are opposite sides of parallelogram *DBCF*. Therefore, $DE = \frac{1}{2}BC$ and $\overline{DE} \parallel \overline{BC}$.

### Further Exploration

If from the midpoint of a side of a triangle a line is drawn parallel to another side, this line bisects the third side.

Although the proof is similar to the preceding one, some students may need your help. Draw $\overline{CF} \parallel \overline{BD}$ and extend $\overline{DE}$ to meet $\overline{CF}$ to form the parallelogram *DBCF*. The rest of the proof is then similar to the preceding proof, but in reverse.

© 2003 Key Curriculum Press

## REASONING BACKWARD: PARALLEL LINES
(PAGE 131)

This worksheet also focuses on the systematization function of proof, since we are proving a result here that was used earlier to prove another result. If you have not yet done so, read the Teacher Notes for the Reasoning Backward: Triangle Midpoints activity.

**Prerequisites:** Knowledge of the AA condition of similarity and the algebra of ratios.

**Sketch:** No sketch is required for this activity. If students wish to reinvestigate this theorem, they can use the sketch **Parallel.gsp.**

### PROVING

1. Angle $ADE$ = angle $ABC$, since they are corresponding and $\overline{DE} \parallel \overline{BC}$.

2. Triangle $ADE$ is similar to triangle $ABC$ (AA).

3. $\frac{AB}{AD} = \frac{AC}{AE}$.

4. $\frac{AD + DB}{AD} = \frac{AE + EC}{AE}$.

5. $\frac{AD + DB}{AD} - \frac{AD}{AD} = \frac{AE + EC}{AE} - \frac{AE}{AE} \longrightarrow \frac{DB}{AD} = \frac{EC}{AE}$.

6. If $D$ is the midpoint of $\overline{AB}$, $E$ will also be the midpoint of $\overline{AC}$. The converse of the triangle midpoint theorem is therefore a special case of this theorem. Similarly, the triangle midpoint theorem itself is a special case of the converse of this theorem (see below).

### Further Exploration

If two sides of a triangle are divided in the same ratios by two points, then a line through those two points will be parallel to the third side.

Although the proof is similar to the previous one (but in reverse order), some students may need your help. The proof follows the answers to Questions 5, 4, and 3, in that order, to show that the triangles are similar by SAS similarity. Conclude, therefore, that corresponding angles $ADE$ and $ABC$ are equal, and hence $\overline{DE} \parallel \overline{BC}$.

## SYSTEMATIZING RHOMBUS PROPERTIES
(PAGE 133)

The main purpose of this activity is to introduce students to the systematization function of proof: the fact that proof is an indispensable tool in the organization of known results into a deductive system of definitions and theorems. Students should know the properties of a rhombus well. It should be made clear to students that the main objective of these worksheets is not to determine whether these properties are true or not, but to investigate their underlying logical relationships, as well as different possible systematizations. However, an element of verification is present, in the sense that the given definitions have to be logically evaluated to see whether all the other properties not included in the definition can be derived from it.

Further objectives are

- Developing students' understanding of the nature of definitions as unproved assumptions, as well as the existence of alternative definitions.

- Engaging students in the evaluation and selection of different formal, economical definitions rather than just providing them with a single ready-made definition.

- Developing students' ability to construct formal, economical definitions for geometrical concepts.

For a more detailed discussion of defining as a mathematical activity and where it fits into the van Hiele theory, read the discussion in the Teacher Notes for the Systematizing Isosceles Trapezoid activity.

**Prerequisites:** Knowledge of the properties of a rhombus, parallel lines, and conditions for congruency.

**Sketch: Rhombus.gsp.**

### DESCRIBE

The purpose of this activity is to introduce students to a mathematical definition as an economical but accurate description of an object.

1. Responses may vary.

2.

| Sketch page | Desc. (a–g) | Comments |
|---|---|---|
| ~~Rhombus 1~~ | b | Point out that this condition is necessary but not sufficient. |
| Rhombus 2 | d | This sketch and description are correct. |
| Rhombus 3 | c | The sketch is correct. Strictly speaking, it is redundant to state that the two axes of symmetry have to be perpendicular, since it can be proven that if a figure has only two axes of symmetry, they are perpendicular to each other. |
| ~~Rhombus 4~~ | a | This description is a necessary, but not sufficient, condition. |
| Rhombus 5 | f | The sketch is correct, and the description is a correct definition. |
| ~~Rhombus 6~~ | e | This sketch constructs a kite. The description is of a necessary, but not sufficient, condition. |
| Rhombus 7 | g | The sketch and description are correct. |

3. c, d, f, and g.

4. Answers will vary, although f is the most economical definion.

5. a. This description is wrong because it contains an *incorrect* property, since rhombuses do not (in general) have equal diagonals.

   b. This one is correct, but *uneconomical* (i.e., it contains more information than is necessary).

   c. This one is *circular;* it is completely unacceptable to define an object in terms of itself, because that does not explain what the object is.

   d. This description does not allow the inclusion of the squares as special cases of rhombuses. Although it is not mathematically incorrect to describe a rhombus in this way, it is *not convenient* to do so. First, a *partition* description (definition) such as this is always longer than an *inclusive* one (because of

having to add qualifiers such as "not all angles equal"). Second, a partition description (definition) invariably increases the number of theorems we have to prove in a deductive system (for example, we have to prove separately that the diagonals of a square bisect each other perpendicularly, instead of just assuming it from an inclusive view in which it is seen as a special rhombus).

## PROVING RHOMBUS PROPERTIES FROM DEFINITIONS

Point out that from the given definition, deductive orderings other than the one given below are possible.

6. They are congruent (SAS).

7. $AB = AD$.

8. They are congruent (SAS).

9. $AB = CB = AD$.

10. They are congruent (SAS).

11. $AD = CD = AB = CB$.

12. They are congruent (SSS). From theorem 1, $AB = AD$, $CB = CD$, and $AC$ is common.

13. Angle $BAC$ = angle $DAC$, and angle $BCA$ = angle $DCA$.

14. They are congruent (SSS).

15. Angle $ABD$ = angle $CBD$, and angle $ADB$ = angle $CDB$.

16. Line $AC$ is an axis of symmetry, since a reflection of triangle $ABC$ around $AC$ maps it onto $ADC$.

17. Line $BD$ is an axis of symmetry, since a reflection of triangle $ABD$ around $BD$ maps it onto $CBD$.

   *Note:* If a rhombus is regarded as a special parallelogram, theorem 4 and its proof are redundant. However, a proof is given simply to show that can it be derived from the given definition.

18. They are congruent (SAS).

19. Angle $BAO$ = angle $DCO$.

20. $\overline{AB} \parallel \overline{CD}$, since the alternate angles $BAO$ and $DCO$ are equal.

21. The argument is similar.

## Further Exploration

1. Responses will vary.

2. Several different possibilities exist; for example:

   a. A rhombus is a parallelogram with one pair of adjacent sides equal (equivalent to g, on the previous page).

   b. A rhombus is a parallelogram with perpendicular diagonals.

   c. A rhombus is a parallelogram with a diagonal bisecting one of its angles.

   d. A rhombus is a kite with one pair of opposite sides parallel.

   e. A rhombus is a kite with three angles bisected by its diagonals.

3. Several different possibilities exist; for example:

   a. A rhombus is a circum quadrilateral with three equal sides.

   b. A rhombus is a circum quadrilateral with opposite sides parallel.

   c. A rhombus is a circum quadrilateral with bisecting diagonals.

   (*Hint:* In all these examples, use the property of a circum quadrilateral that the two sums of its opposite sides are equal.)

   d. A rhombus is a circum quadrilateral with its diagonals intersecting at its incenter.

## Class Discussion

A good definition of a concept is one that allows us to easily deduce the other properties of the concept; that is, it should be *deductive-economical*. It might be a good exercise for students to compare different definitions according to this criterion. For example, the definition of a rhombus as a quadrilateral with two axes of symmetry through the opposite angles is more deductive-economical than the standard textbook definition of it as a quadrilateral with all sides equal. For example, for the former, the other properties (e.g., perpendicular, bisecting diagonals, all sides equal, etc.) follow immediately from symmetry, whereas with the latter, we have to use congruency and somewhat longer arguments to deduce the other properties.

Another way in which we could compare different definitions is to see whether or not a particular definition allows us to directly construct the object being defined. For example, defining a rhombus as any quadrilateral with one pair of adjacent sides equal and opposite sides parallel allows us to construct it easily. However, defining it as a circum quadrilateral with diagonals bisecting at its incenter (although this is valid as a definition) does not allow us to construct it directly from the properties given in the definition. The former definition could be called a *constructable* definition, whereas the latter could be called a *nonconstructable* definition. It is customary (although this is not always done) to choose constructable definitions in mathematics.

# SYSTEMATIZING ISOSCELES TRAPEZOID PROPERTIES (PAGE 139)

The main purpose of this activity is to reinforce the systematization function of proof that was introduced in the activity Systematizing Rhombus Properties—in other words, to show that proof is an indispensable tool in the organization of known results into a deductive system of definitions and theorems. Before doing this activity, students should already have done the Isosceles Trapezoid and Cyclic Quadrilateral activities so that they know the properties of an isosceles trapezoid well. Make clear to students that the main objective in these worksheets is not to determine whether these properties are true or not, but to investigate their underlying logical relationships, as well as different possible systematizations. An element of verification is present, however, in the sense that the given definitions have to be logically evaluated to see whether all the other properties not contained in each definition can be derived from it.

Further objectives are

- Developing students' understanding of the nature of definitions as unproved assumptions, as well as the existence of alternative definitions.

- Engaging students in the construction and selection of different formal, economical definitions rather than just providing them with a single ready-made definition.

- Developing students' ability to construct formal, economical definitions for geometrical concepts.

Constructing definitions is a mathematical activity of no less importance than other mathematical activities, such as conjecturing, generalizing, proving, classifying, developing an algorithm, making deductions from a given definition, and so on. Although we can distinguish between two different types of defining in mathematics, namely *descriptive* (*a posteriori*) and *constructive* defining (*a priori*) (see de Villiers 1986, 1996, 1998a), here we focus mainly on the former.

Descriptive (*a posteriori*) defining here means that the concept (in this case an isosceles trapezoid) and its properties have already been known for some time, and the concept defined only afterward. *A posteriori* defining is usually accomplished by selecting an appropriate subset of the total set of properties of the concept from which all the other properties can be deduced. This subset then serves as the definition, and the other remaining properties are then logically derived from it as theorems.

The purpose of this worksheet is to introduce students to a mathematical definition as an economical but accurate description of an object. Responses to the questions may vary considerably, and some students may need more guidance from you. The purpose here is not for students to produce a single correct, economical definition, but to engage them in the activity of trying out various possibilities. You can expect them to make mistakes such as including too many properties or too few, but only in making such mistakes will they learn what defining is all about.

Although time constraints clearly make it impossible to handle the defining of every quadrilateral in the formal way in which it is done here for isosceles trapezoids, it is important for students (at least once or twice in their mathematical education) to engage in this kind of activity to develop a better understanding of the nature of definitions, as well as their own skill in defining objects on their own.

It should also be noted that students should be at least at van Hiele Level 3 (logical ordering) for this activity. In other words, they should already have completely mastered van Hiele Level 1 (visualization) and van Hiele Level 2 (analysis) with respect to isosceles trapezoids. Making constructions to test their own (or the given) definition helps them to see the interrelationships between properties, namely, that some properties *imply* others—a fundamental characteristic of van Hiele Level 3. In other words, these constructions are psychologically important in that they develop explicit understanding of *if-then* relationships; that is, *if* we construct a cyclic quadrilateral with equal diagonals, *then* it will have at least one axis of symmetry, at least one pair of opposite sides parallel, at least one pair of opposite sides equal, and so on.

**Prerequisites:** Isosceles Trapezoid and Cyclic Quadrilateral activities. Knowledge of conditions for congruency, properties of cyclic quadrilaterals, and parallelograms.

**Sketch: Iso Trap.gsp.**

## DESCRIBE

1. Responses will vary.

2. Responses will vary.

3. Testing these descriptions by construction is important not only for checking their accuracy, but also for developing understanding of the logical *if-then* relationships between the properties of an isosceles trapezoid.

| Sketch page | Desc. (a–d) | Comments |
|---|---|---|
| ~~Iso Trap 1~~ | a | Point out that this condition is necessary, but not sufficient. |
| Iso Trap 2 | d | The sketch and description are correct. Note that for technical reasons having to do with the way Sketchpad constructs circle intersections, the convex figure cannot be dragged into the crossed case (degenerating instead into a triangle). |
| ~~Iso Trap 3~~ | c | This description is ambiguous because it can include parallelograms. |
| Iso Trap 4 | a | This sketch is correct. It corresponds to a corrected version of the incomplete description in (a) and includes the additional property that at least one pair of sides are parallel. Note that the figure that this construction creates can be crossed. |
| Iso Trap 5 | b | This sketch is correct. The description is uneconomical because the property that adjacent angles are equal is a consequence of the symmetry and is thus redundant in the description. Note that the figure this construction creates can be crossed. |

4. The Iso trap 4 page of the sketch improves description (a), which is incorrect, by changing it to the following:

An isosceles trapezoid is any quadrilateral with at least one pair of opposite sides parallel and equal diagonals.

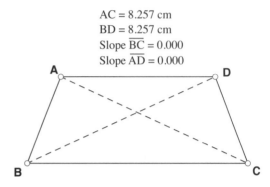

AC = 8.257 cm
BD = 8.257 cm
Slope $\overline{BC}$ = 0.000
Slope $\overline{AD}$ = 0.000

Point out that the statement "an isosceles trapezoid is a quadrilateral with equal diagonals" is a correct statement about a property of isosceles trapezoids, but that it contains too little information to be used as a description (definition). We would therefore say that "equal diagonals" is a necessary, but not sufficient, condition for isosceles trapezoids. One way of correcting an incomplete description (definition) is to include more properties, as we have done here.

Note that this improved description includes a *crossed* isosceles trapezoid, as shown by the figure below (which has *all* the properties of a convex one). However, if we allow crossed quadrilaterals, strictly speaking we have to specify that the equal diagonals have to be *nonparallel;* otherwise we could get a crossed quadrilateral, as shown by the figure on the top of the next page, that is *not* an isosceles trapezoid. Also note that this crossed quadrilateral is not a parallelogram, since one pair of opposite sides ($\overline{AB}$ and $\overline{CD}$) are not parallel, but intersect.

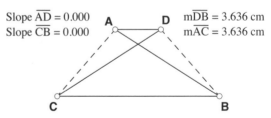

Slope $\overline{AD}$ = 0.000
Slope $\overline{CB}$ = 0.000

m$\overline{DB}$ = 3.636 cm
m$\overline{AC}$ = 3.636 cm

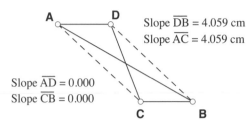

Slope $\overline{DB}$ = 4.059 cm
Slope $\overline{AC}$ = 4.059 cm

Slope $\overline{AD}$ = 0.000
Slope $\overline{CB}$ = 0.000

5. Description (b). An isosceles trapezoid is any quadrilateral with at least one axis of symmetry through a pair of opposite sides. The property that adjacent angles are equal is a consequence of the symmetry and is thus redundant in the description. Note that this description (definition) includes the *crossed* case, which can be obtained with a sketch based on the Iso Trap 5 page of the sketch if one of the vertices is dragged across the line of symmetry.

Point out that in general a correct, but uneconomical, description (definition) that contains too much information can be improved by leaving out some of the properties. However, we must still be sure that the conditions are sufficient. For example, if we leave out the axis of symmetry property, the description (definition) is incorrect, since it is possible to construct a quadrilateral with one pair of adjacent angles equal that is not an isosceles trapezoid (see figure).

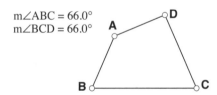

m∠ABC = 66.0°
m∠BCD = 66.0°

If they are allowed to choose their own descriptions (definitions), many students tend to intuitively choose description (c):

> An isosceles trapezoid is any quadrilateral with at least one pair of parallel sides and at least one pair of opposite sides equal.

However, it is unacceptable, because it is ambiguous. For example, although we can obtain an isosceles trapezoid as shown in the first figure that follows, the description also includes parallelograms as shown by the other two figures. Explain that a (general) parallelogram *cannot* be considered an isosceles trapezoid, since it does not have all the

necessary properties (equal diagonals, two pairs of adjacent angles equal, cyclic, axis of symmetry, etc.).

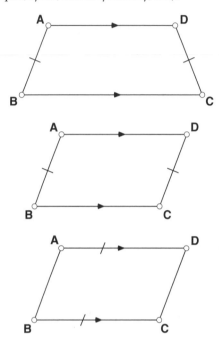

There is no satisfactory way to correct this definition. If we formulate it in such a way as to exclude the parallelograms—for example, "An isosceles trapezoid is any quadrilateral with one pair of opposite sides parallel and another pair of opposite sides equal, but not parallel"—we exclude not only the (general) parallelogram cases 2 and 3, but also the rectangles and squares, from the set of isosceles trapezoids. But as we have seen in the Isosceles Trapezoid activity, it is convenient to consider rectangles and squares to be special cases of isosceles trapezoids. (Also see the discussion in Question 6e below.)

Description (d) is a correct, economical description (definition):

> An isosceles trapezoid is any cyclic quadrilateral with at least one pair of opposite sides parallel.

Although this definition includes the crossed case as before, a sketch based on the Iso Trap 2 page of the sketch unfortunately does not allow the dynamic transformation from a convex quadrilateral to a crossed one.

6. a. This description (definition) is wrong because it contains an incorrect property, since isosceles

trapezoids do not in general have perpendicular diagonals.

b. This description is circular; it is completely unacceptable to describe (define) an object in terms of itself, because such a description does not explain what the object is.

c. This description is ambiguous; that is, it easily lends itself to misinterpretation. First, it does not say how many pairs of adjacent angles are equal: Is it one or two? Second, even if we specify that it is only two pairs, it is still confusing. For example, a quadrilateral has four pairs of adjacent angles (for example, $A$ and $B$, $B$ and $C$, $C$ and $D$, and $D$ and $A$). So clearly we could have a quad with two pairs of adjacent angles equal that is not an isosceles trapezoid, as shown below ($A = B$, $B = C$, and $C = D$).

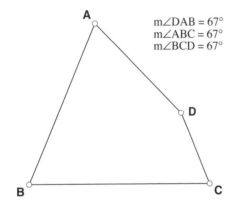

m∠DAB = 67°
m∠ABC = 67°
m∠BCD = 67°

d. This description is uneconomical. Point out that we could list all the properties of a concept that we want to describe (define), but it is common practice to keep a description (definition) as short as possible. Emphasize that a good description (definition) avoids unnecessary information; it must be economical. We therefore usually do not include in our mathematical descriptions (definitions) *all* the properties of a set of objects being defined, but only *necessary* properties to ensure that we obtain the elements of that set. However, more serious than including too much information is including too little, in which case there are objects that comply with the description (definition), but are not elements of the set we want to define. In other words, for a description (definition) to be correct,

it must contain *sufficient* properties to ensure that we obtain not only the elements of the set we want to define, but only those elements (not any others).

e. This is a partition description (definition), which does not allow for the inclusion of rectangles and squares. Point out that a partition description (definition) is *not* mathematically wrong; it is simply less convenient than an inclusive one (see de Villiers 1994). For example, an inclusive definition is invariably shorter (more economical), since the partition definition has to include additional properties (for example, not all angles equal) to ensure that the rectangles and squares are excluded. An inclusive definition is also more economical from a deductive point of view. For example, if we define an isosceles trapezoid so that it allows the inclusion of the rectangles and squares as special cases, it immediately follows that rectangles and squares also have equal diagonals. However, if we used a partition definition for an isosceles trapezoid, we could not immediately conclude this, and we would have to prove that a rectangle and a square also have equal diagonals. This is clearly uneconomical, since we would then have to construct three separate proofs, instead of just the one proof required with an inclusive definition.

Research in traditional geometry education (without dynamic geometry software) has shown that many students spontaneously prefer partition definitions to inclusive definitions in relation to quadrilaterals. (For example, a typical response is for them to define a rectangle as a quadrilateral with all angles equal, but not all sides equal, so as to exclude squares.) This is due in part to the static way in which quadrilaterals have been traditionally experienced by students.

However, with the availability of software such as Sketchpad, it is conceivable that students will have far less difficulty accepting class inclusions. For example, in the earlier investigations of isosceles trapezoids, students should already have noticed that an isosceles trapezoid can be dynamically dragged into the shape of a rectangle or a square; in other words, rectangles and squares are special isosceles trapezoids. So although inclusive defining (hierarchical classifying) is considered in the van Hiele theory as a distinctive feature of the third level, it would appear that within a properly designed Sketchpad environment, students should have little difficulty accepting special cases at the visualization level (Level 1).

**CHALLENGE** It is not expected here that students will actually arrive at correct proofs or do a complete, correct systematization, but it is important that they be encouraged to try to prove on their own that one or two properties can be deduced from these descriptions (definitions).

## PROVING ISOSCELES TRAPEZOID PROPERTIES FROM DEFINITIONS

Most students will need some help and guidance in this section, although the stronger ones should be able to cope on their own. Point out that the systematization that follows is not unique; systematizations may differ in their modes of *presentation* (for example, we could instead use two-column proofs), *organization* (we could first prove theorem 2 and then use it to prove theorem 1), or *argument* (we could use a congruency argument instead of symmetry in a particular proof).

7. Angles *A* and *C* are supplementary, since *ABCD* is cyclic.

8. Angles *A* and *B* are also supplementary, since they are interior angles of $\overline{AB}$, the transversal to the parallels $\overline{AD}$ and $\overline{BC}$.

9. Therefore, angle *B* = angle *C*.

10. In the same way, it follows that angle *A* = angle *D*.

11. Angle *DEC* = angle *ABE* (corresponding angles with $\overline{DE} \parallel \overline{AB}$).

12. Angle *ABE* = angle *DCE*.

13. Therefore, angle *DEC* = angle *DCE*.

14. Thus, triangle *DEC* is isosceles and *DC* = *DE*.

15. *ABED* is a parallelogram, since opposite sides are parallel.

16. *DE* = *AB*.

17. Therefore, *AB* = *DC*.

18. Triangles *ABC* and *DCB* are congruent (SAS). ($\overline{BC}$ is common, *AB* = *DC* (proved), and angle *B* = angle *C* (proved).)

19. Therefore, *AC* = *DB*.

   *Note:* This theorem can also be proved quite elegantly as follows: From theorem 1, we have angle *ABC* = angle *DCB*. But since equal angles are subtended by equal chords, it follows that the two chords subtending these two angles must be equal; that is, *AC* = *DB*.

20. *m*∠ *BFE* = 90°, since $\overline{AD} \parallel \overline{BC}$ and angle *BFE* is co-interior with the right angle *AEF*.

21. Triangles *ABE* and *DCE* are congruent (SAS). (*AB* = *DC* (proved), *AE* = *DE* ($\overline{EF}$ is perpendicular bisector), and angle *A* = angle *D* (proved).)

22. Therefore, *BE* = *CE*.

23. Triangles *EBF* and *ECF* are congruent (90°, S, S). (*EF* is common, *BE* = *CE* (proved), and angle *BFE* = 90° = angle *CFE* (proved).)

24. Therefore, *BF* = *CF*.

25. The line through $\overline{EF}$ is an axis of symmetry, since reflecting over it would map *A* to *D* and *B* to *C*.

## Systematize More

A possible example for each of the two definitions A and B is given below.

A. *Definition:* An isosceles trapezoid is any quadrilateral with at least one pair of parallel sides and equal diagonals.

   **Theorem 1:** An isosceles trapezoid has at least one pair of opposite sides equal.

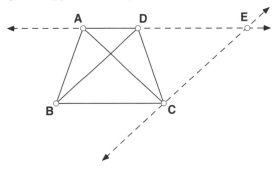

   **Proof:** Consider the figure above where it is given that $\overline{AD} \parallel \overline{BC}$ and *AC* = *BD*. Draw line *CE* parallel to *BD*

as shown. Then *BCED* is a parallelogram; therefore, *BD* = *CE* (opposite sides) and angle *DBC* = angle *AEC* (opposite angles). But triangle *ACE* is isosceles; therefore, angle *AEC* = angle *EAC*. But angle *EAC* = alternate angle *ACB*; therefore, angle *DBC* = angle *ACB*. Triangles *ACB* and *DBC* are therefore congruent (SAS). Thus, *AB* = *DC*.

**Theorem 2:** An isosceles trapezoid has two (distinct) pairs of adjacent angles equal.

**Proof:** Consider the same figure. From the congruency of triangles *ACB* and *DBC*, it follows that angle *ABC* = angle *DCB*. From theorem 1, we now also have triangles *ABD* and *DCA* congruent (SSS). Therefore, angle *BAD* = angle *CDA*.

**Theorem 3:** An isosceles trapezoid is cyclic.

**Proof:** Consider the same figure. From theorem 2, we have angle *ABC* = angle *DCB*. But $m\angle BAD + m\angle ABC = 180°$ (co-interior angles); therefore, $m\angle BAD + m\angle DCB = 180°$, which implies that *ABCD* is cyclic.

**Theorem 4:** An isosceles trapezoid has at least one axis of symmetry through a pair of opposite sides.

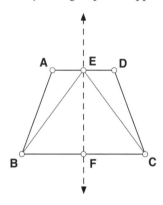

**Proof:** Consider the figure. Construct the perpendicular bisector of $\overline{AD}$ at *E* as shown, and label its intersection with $\overline{BC}$ as *F*. We now have to prove that this line is also the perpendicular bisector of $\overline{BC}$, and therefore an axis of symmetry of *ABCD*. Since $\overline{AD} \parallel \overline{BC}$, we have $m\angle BFE = 90°$. Triangles *ABE* and *DCE* are congruent (SAS); therefore, *BE* = *CE*. Thus, triangles *EBF* and *ECF* are congruent (90°, S, S).

Therefore, *BF* = *CF* and the line through $\overline{EF}$ is an axis of symmetry, since reflecting over it would map *A* to *D* and *B* to *C*.

B. *Definition:* An isosceles trapezoid is any quadrilateral with at least one axis of symmetry through a pair of opposite sides.

**Theorem 1:** An isosceles trapezoid has at least one pair of opposite sides equal.

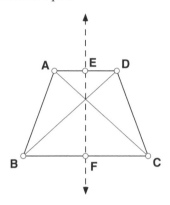

**Proof:** Consider the figure above where it is given that $\overleftrightarrow{EF}$ is a line of symmetry of *ABCD*. A reflection of $\overline{AB}$ over line *EF* clearly maps it onto $\overline{CD}$; therefore, *AB* = *DC*.

**Theorem 2:** An isosceles trapezoid has two (distinct) pairs of adjacent angles equal.

**Proof:** Consider the same figure. A reflection of angles *A* and *B* over line *EF* clearly maps them respectively onto angles *D* and *C*; therefore, these two sets of angles are equal.

**Theorem 3:** An isosceles trapezoid has equal diagonals.

**Proof:** Consider the same figure. A reflection of $\overline{AC}$ over line $\overline{EF}$ clearly maps it onto $\overline{DB}$ (*A* maps to *D*, and *C* maps to *B*); therefore, *AC* = *DB*.

**Theorem 4:** An isosceles trapezoid has at least one pair of opposite sides parallel.

**Proof:** Consider the same figure. By the definition of symmetry, $m\angle AEF = 90° = m\angle BFE$; therefore, $\overline{AD} \parallel \overline{BC}$.

**Theorem 5:** An isosceles trapezoid is cyclic.

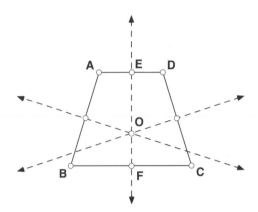

**Proof:** Consider the figure above. All that must be shown for *ABCD* to be cyclic is that its perpendicular bisectors are concurrent. Note first that the perpendicular bisectors of $\overline{AD}$ and $\overline{BC}$ coincide. Construct the perpendicular bisector of $\overline{AB}$ and label its intersection with line *EF* as *O*. Since a reflection of $\overline{AB}$ over line $\overline{EF}$ maps it onto $\overline{DC}$, their respective perpendicular bisectors must also map onto each other over line *EF* at *O*. Therefore, the perpendicular bisectors are concurrent at *O* and *ABCD* is cyclic. (*Note:* We could also, alternatively, use theorems 2 and 4 to show that opposite angles are supplementary, but it is insightful to show via symmetry why it is cyclic.)

## Explore Further Definitions

Remind students that there are essentially two ways of evaluating the correctness of a mathematical definition of a geometric figure:

i. By accurate construction and measurement (to check whether we can construct the intended figure and whether it always remains that figure).

ii. By proof (using logical deduction to check whether all the properties not included in the definition can be derived from it).

Students could first try to construct an isosceles trapezoid from these definitions to test whether they include sufficient conditions. If the constructed figure is not always an isosceles trapezoid, students should correct their definitions by including more properties. If students do not use all the properties given in a definition, but nevertheless correctly construct an isosceles trapezoid, it is obvious that the "unused" properties were not necessary. Such definitions

can then be made more economical by removing any such "unused" properties.

The investigation of these definitions is optional, although it may be invaluable in consolidating the ideas and skills developed in the preceding worksheets. Some students may not need to first make Sketchpad sketches and will easily suspect the truth or falsity of each definition and move directly to the production of a proof or a counterexample. Other students will probably need some help with the design and construction of appropriate Sketchpad sketches.

1. This definition is correct and economical for a convex cyclic quadrilateral, but not for a crossed one as shown by the counterexample below.

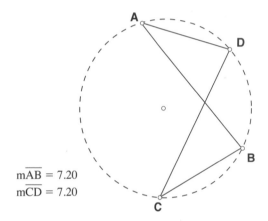

$\text{m}\overline{AB} = 7.20$
$\text{m}\overline{CD} = 7.20$

(*Hint:* Use the property that equal chords subtend equal angles to prove it for the convex case.)

2. This definition is correct and economical.

3. This definition is incorrect, because we can obtain figures from it that are not isosceles trapezoids. For example, although the first arrangement of the sides and angles on the next page would give an isosceles trapezoid, the second one would not necessarily do so.

AD = 3.8 cm      m∠ADC = 61°
BC = 3.8 cm      m∠BCD = 61°

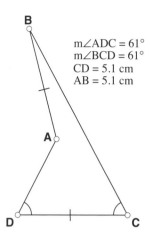

m∠ADC = 61°
m∠BCD = 61°
CD = 5.1 cm
AB = 5.1 cm

4. This definition is also incorrect, because we can obtain figures from it that are not isosceles trapezoids. For example, although the first arrangement below of the angles and parallel lines would give an isosceles trapezoid, the second one would not necessarily do so.

m∠ADC = 61°   Slope $\overline{CD}$ = 0.0
m∠BCD = 61°   Slope $\overline{AB}$ = 0.0

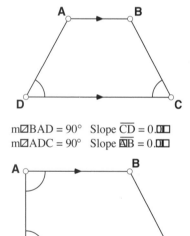

m∠BAD = 90°   Slope $\overline{CD}$ = 0.0▯
m∠ADC = 90°   Slope $\overline{AB}$ = 0.0▯

The definition can, however, be made more precise. For example, we could state that the two equal adjacent angles also have to both be adjacent to one of the parallel sides.

5. This definition is correct and economical. (By *distinct* we mean here *nonoverlapping*.) Although all the other properties can easily be logically deduced from this definition, note that it is not possible to make a

dynamic construction on Sketchpad using only these properties. For example, if we in general constructed two *arbitrary* pairs of angles equal, we would obtain a figure *ABCDE* as shown below, which would form a quadrilateral only when rays $\overrightarrow{AE}$ and $\overrightarrow{DE}$ coincided; in other words, if angles at *A* and *B* were supplementary (but then we would be including an additional property). Such a definition can be called a *nonconstructable* definition, since it is not possible to directly construct the concept only from the conditions contained in the definition. (*Note:* Though not constructable directly from the definition, it is easy to prove that the angles at *A* and *B* must be supplementary from the given conditions. If the angles at *A* and *D* are equal to *x* and those at *B* and *C* equal to *y*, it follows that for a (simple closed) quadrilateral $2x + 2y = 360° → x + y = 180°$.)

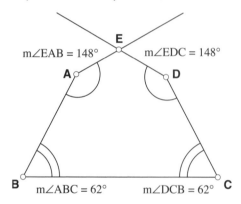

m∠EAB = 148°          m∠EDC = 148°

m∠ABC = 62°          m∠DCB = 62°

6. This definition is correct and economical for a convex quadrilateral, but not for a crossed one, as shown by the counterexample below.

m$\overline{AB}$ = 3.95 cm
m$\overline{CD}$ = 3.95 cm
m$\overline{AC}$ = 4.24 cm
m$\overline{BD}$ = 4.24 cm

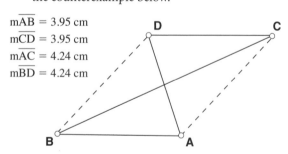

## Class Discussion

A good definition of a concept is one that allows us to easily deduce the other properties of a concept; that is, it should be *deductive-economical*. It might be a good exercise for students to compare the different definitions according to this criterion. For example, the definition of an isosceles trapezoid in terms of its axis of symmetry through a pair of opposite sides provides the simplest way of deducing the remaining properties from it; that is, they virtually all follow directly from the symmetry property. In contrast, other possible definitions require certain constructions or the use of longer or more complicated arguments.

Another standard by which we could compare different definitions is whether or not a particular definition allows us to directly construct the object being defined. For example, defining an isosceles trapezoid as any cyclic quadrilateral with at least one pair of opposite sides equal allows us to easily construct it. However, defining it as any quadrilateral with two distinct pairs of adjacent angles equal does not allow us to directly construct it from the properties included in the definition. The former definition could be called a *constructable* definition, whereas the latter could be called a *nonconstructable* definition. It is customary (although it is not always done) to choose constructable definitions in mathematics.

## Defining and Investigating New Concepts

These two questions respectively involve the specialization and generalization of the concept of the isosceles trapezoid. These are examples of the mathematical process of *constructive* defining, whereby new objects are defined by modifying or extending the definitions of known objects.

1. The diagonals *DB* and *AC* respectively bisect angles *ABC* and *DCB*.

   **Proof:** Consider the figure below. $m\angle CBD = m\angle ABD$ (equal chords *CD* and *AD* subtend equal angles). Similarly, $m\angle BCA = m\angle DCA$.

   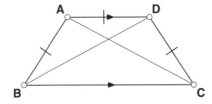

2. a. The two sums of alternate angles of an isosceles hexagon are equal.

   **Proof:** Consider the following figure. By symmetry, $m\angle A = m\angle F$, $m\angle B = m\angle E$, and $m\angle C = m\angle D$. Therefore, $m\angle A + m\angle C + m\angle E = m\angle B + m\angle D + m\angle F$.

   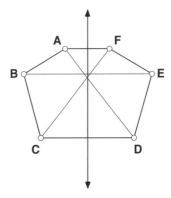

   In general, for any $2n$-gon ($n > 1$), the two sums of the measures of the alternate angles are equal, and this follows directly from symmetry.

   b. One pair of "diagonals" of an isosceles hexagon are equal.

   **Proof:** Consider the figure above. By symmetry, $AD = FC$.

   In general, for any $2n$-gon, ($n > 1$) there are ($n/2$) pairs of equal "diagonals," and this follows directly from symmetry.

# References

Albers, D. J. 1982. Paul Halmos: Maverick mathologist. *The Two-Year College Mathematics Journal* 13 (4): 234–241.

Alibert, D. 1988. Towards new customs in the classroom. *For the Learning of Mathematics* 8 (2): 31–35; 43.

Bell, A. W. 1976. A study of pupils' proof-explanations in mathematical situations. *Educational Studies in Mathematics* 7: 23–40.

Burger, W. F., and J. M. Shaughnessy, 1986. Characterizing the van Hiele levels of development in geometry. *Journal for Research in Mathematics Education* 17 (1): 31–48.

Coxeter, H. S. M., and S. L. Greitzer. 1967. *Geometry revisited*. Washington, D.C.: Mathematical Association of America.

Davis, P. J. 1976. The nature of proof. In *Proceedings of the fifth international congress on mathematical education,* edited by M. Carss. Boston: Birkhauser.

Davis, P. J., and R. Hersh. 1983. *The mathematical experience*. Great Britain: Pelican Books.

———. 1986. *Descartes' dream*. New York: Harcourt Brace Jovanovich.

Deer, G. W. 1969. The effects of teaching an explicit unit in logic on students' ability to prove theorems in geometry. Unpublished doctoral dissertation, Florida State University. *Dissertation Abstracts International* 30: 387–399.

de Jager, C. J. 1990. When should we use pattern? *Pythagoras* 23: 11–14.

de Villiers, M. D. 1986. The role of axiomatization in mathematics and mathematics teaching. *RUMEUS Studies in Mathematics Education No. 2.* Stellenbosch, South Africa: Research Unit for Mathematics Education of the University of Stellenbosch (RUMEUS).

———. 1988. What happens if? Why? *Pythagoras* 18: 45–47.

———. 1991. Pupils' needs for conviction and explanation within the context of geometry. *Pythagoras* 26: 18–27.

———. 1994. The role and function of a hierarchical classification of the quadrilaterals. *For the Learning of Mathematics* 14 (1): 11–18.

———. 1996. *Some adventures in Euclidean geometry.* Durban, South Africa: University of Durban-Westville.

———. 1997. The role of proof in investigative, computer-based geometry: Some personal reflections. In *Geometry Turned On!* edited by D. Schattschneider and J. King. Washington, D.C.: Mathematical Association of America.

———. 1998a. Dual generalizations of van Aubel's theorem. *The Mathematical Gazette* 82 (495) (Nov): 405–412.

———. 1998b. To teach definitions in geometry or teach to define? In Olivier, A., and K. Newstead, eds., *Proceedings of 22nd PME-Conference*, University of Stellenbosch, South Africa, 12–17 July 1998, vol. 2: 248–255.

———. 1999a. A further generalization of the Fermat-Torricelli point. *The Mathematical Gazette* 83 (496) (March): 14–16.

———. 1999b. A Sketchpad discovery involving areas of inscribed polygons. *Mathematics in School* 28 (1) (March): 18–21.

———. 2000. Generalizing van Aubel using duality. *Mathematics Magazine* 73 (4) (Oct): 303–306.

Donaldson, M. 1979. *Children's minds.* New York: W. W. Norton.

Fischbein, E. 1982. Intuition and proof. *For the Learning of Mathematics* 3 (2): 9–18.

Freudenthal, H., ed. 1958. *Report on methods of initiation into geometry.* Groningen: Wolters.

Freudenthal, H. 1973. *Mathematics as an educational task.* Dordrecht: D. Reidel.

Fuys, D., D. Geddes, and R. Tischler. 1988. The van Hiele model of thinking in geometry among adolescents. *JRME Monograph No. 3*, Washington, D.C.: National Council of Teachers of Mathematics.

Gale, M. D. 1990. Proof as explanation. *The Mathematical Intelligence.* 12 (1): 4.

Gonobolin, F. N. 1954. Pupils' comprehension of geometric proofs. In Wilson, J. W., ed., 1975, *Soviet Studies in the Psychology of Learning and Teaching Mathematics.* Vol. 12, Problems of Instruction. Chicago: University of Chicago.

Govender, R., and M. D. de Villiers. 2002. Formulation and evaluation of definitions in a Sketchpad context. Paper presented at AMESA 2002, Durban, South Africa.

Griffiths, H. B., and A. G. Howson. 1974. *Mathematics: Society and curricula.* London: Cambridge University Press.

Grünbaum, B., and G. C. Shephard. 1995. Ceva, Menelaus, and the area principle. *Mathematics Magazine* 68 (4) (Oct): 254–268.

Hanna, G. 1983. *Rigorous proof in mathematics education.* Toronto: OISE Press.

———. 1989. More than formal proof. *For the Learning of Mathematics* 9 (1): 20–23.

Hewson, S. N. P. 1977. Inferential problem solving in young children. Unpublished doctoral dissertation, Oxford University.

Hildebrandt, S., and A. Tromba. 1985. *Mathematics of Optimal Form.* New York: Scientific American Library of W. H. Freeman & Co.

Hull, L. W. H. 1969. The superstition of educated men. *Mathematics Teaching* 43: 26–31.

Human, P. G. 1978. Wiskundige werkwyses in Wiskunde-onderwys. Unpublished doctoral dissertation, University of Stellenbosch.

Human, P. G., and J. H. Nel. 1989. In cooperation with M. D. de Villiers, T. P. Dreyer, and S. F. G. Wessels. *USEME curriculum material.* Research Unit for Mathematics Education of the University of Stellenbosch (RUMEUS).

Human, P. G., and J. H. Nel. 1997. In cooperation with M. D. de Villiers, T. P. Dreyer, and S. F. G. Wessels. Alternative instructional strategies in geometry education: A theoretical and empirical study. A translation of the theoretical part of the final report on the USEME project by the Research Unit for Mathematics Education of the University of Stellenbosch (RUMEUS) can be downloaded from http://mzone.mweb.co.za/residents/profmd/homepage4.html [October 7, 2002].

Johnson, R. A. 1929. *Advanced Euclidean geometry.* New York: Dover Publications.

Kelly. P. J. 1966. Van Aubel's quadrilateral theorem. *Mathematics Magazine* 39: 35–37.

Keyton, M. 1997. Students discovering geometry using dynamic software. In *Geometry turned on! Dynamic software in learning, teaching and research,* edited by J. King and D. Schattschneider. Washington, D.C.: Mathematical Association of America: 63–68.

King, J. 1997. An eye for similarity transformations. In *Geometry Turned On!* edited by D. Schattschneider and J. King. Washington, D.C.: Mathematical Association of America.

Klein, F. 1925. *Elementary mathematics from an advanced standpoint.* New York: Macmillan.

Kline, M. 1973. *Why Johnny can't add: The failure of the new math.* New York: St. Martin's Press.

———. 1985. Mathematics for the nonmathematician. New York: Dover Publications.

Krygowska, A. Z. 1971. Treatment of the axiomatic method in class. In *Teaching school mathematics,* edited by W. Servais and T. Varga. London: Penguin-Unesco. 124–150.

Lakatos, I. 1976. *Proof and refutations.* Cambridge; New York: Cambridge University Press.

Manin, Y. I. 1981. A digression on proof. *The Two-Year College Mathematics Journal* 12 (2): 104–107.

© 2003 Key Curriculum Press

# References

The Mathematical Association of South Africa. 1978. *South African Mathematics Project: Syllabus Proposals.* Pretoria: MASA. (Now Centrahil: AMESA).

Movshovitz-Hadar, N. and J. Webb. 1998. *One Equals Zero.* Emeryville, CA: Key Curriculum Press.

Mudaly, V. 1998. Pupils' needs for conviction and explanation within the context of dynamic geometry. Unpublished M.Ed. dissertation, University of Durban-Westville.

Mudaly, V., and M. de Villiers. 2000. Learners' needs for conviction and explanation within the context of dynamic geometry. *Pythagoras* 52 (August): 20–23.

Mueller, D. J. 1975. Logic and the ability to prove theorems in geometry. Unpublished doctoral dissertation, Florida State University. *Dissertation Abstracts International* 36: 851A.

Polya, G. 1919. L'Enseignment mathematique, no. 4: 355–379.

———. 1954. *Mathematics and plausible reasoning. Vol. 1, Induction and analogy in mathematics.* Princeton, NJ: Princeton University Press.

———. 1981. *Mathematical discovery: On understanding, learning, and teaching problem solving* (2 vols.). New York: John Wiley and Sons.

Renz, P. 1981. Mathematical proof: What it is and what it ought to be. *The Two-Year College Mathematics Journal* 12 (2): 83–103.

Rota, Gian-Carlo. 1997. Indescrete thoughts. Boston: Birkhauser.

Schoenfeld, A. H. 1986. On having and using geometric knowledge. In *Conceptual and procedural knowledge: The case of mathematics,* edited by J. Hiebert. Hillsdale, NJ: L. Erlbaum Associates.

Sharygin, I. 2000. Two articles and two hundred problems. Paper presented at ICME 9, Japan.

Smith, R. R. 1940. Three major difficulties in the learning of demonstrative geometry. *The Mathematics Teacher* 33: 99–134; 150–178.

Tall, D. 1989. The nature of mathematical proof. *Mathematics Teaching* 127 (June): 28–32.

van Asch, A. G. 1993. To prove, why and how? *International Journal of Mathematics Education in Science and Technology* 24 (2): 301–313.

van Dormolen, J. 1977. Learning to understand what giving a proof really means. *Educational Studies in Mathematics* 8: 27–34.

van Hiele, P. M. 1973. *Begrip en Inzicht.* Purmerend, Netherlands: Muusses.

Volmink, J. D. 1990. The nature and role of proof in mathematics education. *Pythagoras* 23: 7–10.

Wallington, B. A. 1974. Some aspects of the development of reasoning in preschool children. Unpublished doctoral dissertation, University of Edinburgh.

Walter, R. L. 1972. The effect of knowledge of logic in proving mathematical theorems in the context of mathematical induction. Unpublished doctoral dissertation, Florida State University. *Dissertation Abstracts International* 33: 262A.

Wason, P. C., and P. N. Johnson-Laird, 1972. *Psychology of reasoning: Structure and content.* London: Batsford.

Wilder, R. L. 1944. The nature of mathematical proof. *American Mathematical Monthly* 51: 309–323.

Winicki-Landman, G. 2001. Research of original geometric concepts: some episodes from the classroom. *International Journal of Mathematical Education in Science and Technology* 32 (5): 727–744.

Yaglom, I. M. 1962. *Geometric transformations I.* Washington, D.C.: Mathematical Association of America.